VANCOUVER KIDS

THE COURAGEOUS KIDS SERIES

Vancouver
KIDS

Lesley McKnight

Charlotte,
Pleasure to meet
you!

BRINDLE
& GLASS

Copyright © 2011 Lesley McKnight

Brindle & Glass Publishing Ltd.
www.brindleandglass.com

Library and Archives Canada Cataloguing in Publication
McKnight, Lesley, 1974–
Vancouver kids / Lesley McKnight.

Print format: ISBN 978-1-897142-52-3
Electronic monograph in PDF format: ISBN 978-1-897142-61-5
Electronic monograph in HTML format: ISBN 978-1-897142-62-2

1. Children—British Columbia—Vancouver—Juvenile literature.
2. Vancouver (BC)—History—Juvenile literature. I. Title.

FC3847.33.M35 2011   j971.1'33   C2010-906361-9

Editor: Linda Goyette
Proofreader: Holland Gidney
Front cover: Vancouver skyline by Duncan Tidd, stck.xchng
Cover design: Pete Kohut
Author photo: Janette Ahrens

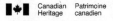

Brindle & Glass is pleased to acknowledge the financial support for its publishing program from the Government of Canada through the Canada Book Fund, Canada Council for the Arts, and the Province of British Columbia through the British Columbia Arts Council and the Book Publishing Tax Credit.

The interior pages of this book have been printed on 100% post-consumer recycled paper, processed chlorine free, and printed with vegetable-based inks.

1 2 3 4 5 14 13 12 11

PRINTED IN CANADA

To my three favourite Vancouver kids and their dad.

The Stories

For a glossary of words used in *Vancouver Kids*, and for more information about the *Courageous Kids* series, visit courageouskids.ca.

GREATER VANCOUVER AREA (Map A)

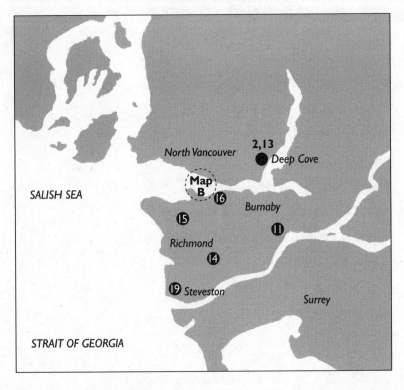

North Vancouver

2,13
● Deep Cove

SALISH SEA

Map B ⑯

Burnaby

⑮

⑪

Richmond

⑭

⑲ Steveston

Surrey

STRAIT OF GEORGIA

List of Locations for Each Story

❶ **The Two Sisters:** (imagined)

❷ **Why I Loathe Captain Vancouver:** Beach where Thomas Pitt slept (Map A)

❸ **Child Bride:** Deighton House, (Map B)

❹ **Story Blankets:** Silvey Home (Map B)

❺ **Vancouver is Burning!** End of Carrall Street (Map B)

❻ **The Intruders:** Chaythoos (Map B)

❼ **That Fearsome Iron Horse:** Kanaka Ranch (Map B)

❽ **The Bear That Saw Lace Underwear:** Avison Residence (Map B)

❾ **My Lucky Automobile Accident:** Roedde House (Museum) (Map B)

❿ **House Girl:** Chinatown (Map B)

VANCOUVER (Map B)

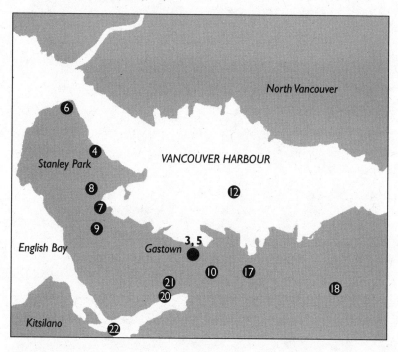

Introduction

A promise to readers

I remember sitting in a class about Canadian history, and feeling so sleepy that I wondered if toothpicks could hold my eyelids open the way they do in cartoons. I'm glad I never tried that because I think it would have hurt.

Imagine how surprised I was to find out a few years later that I loved history. I adore stories and that's all history is—a collection of stories about the past. Hey, the word "story" is hiding right there in the word "history." The past can mean yesterday, last week, a hundred years ago, or longer. You name it—if it's over, it's history. If you came home from school yesterday and told someone about your day, you were documenting history. You historian, you.

The stories in this book are about Vancouver's history from a perspective that I think is too often ignored. All of the stories in this book are told by kids. If you live in Vancouver, or have visited it, you are a part of Vancouver's history too.

I am a Vancouver kid myself. I moved here when I was thirteen, thinking I was the luckiest person ever. I gobbled up the city, big mouthfuls at a time. I wanted to see all of it, from the tiny alleys of Chinatown to the entire length of the seawall. My new friends laughed when I became so distracted by the gorgeous views from the top of Grouse Mountain that I had trouble learning how to ski. Taking a water taxi to shop for food on Granville Island was so much more exotic than going by bus to an ordinary grocery store (even though we did that too).

On a sunny day, Vancouver shines. I head down to Spanish Banks, stake out a spot on the beach, and soak it all in. I look towards downtown and I imagine the corner of Robson and Burrard, cars streaming by and pedestrians twenty deep on each street corner. I squint over at the North Shore seawall and I picture the steady flow of bikes, strollers and rollerbladers. Then I look up to the top of the mountains. I close my eyes and imagine the quiet of the peaks with the wind swirling and the clouds overhead.

Vancouverites like to grumble about the rain, but I don't mind it. The city looks different when it rains. One of my favourite things to do is to find a window seat in a café. I peer out at the passersby. I try to imagine where people are going and where they are coming from. I wonder about their stories. There are more than two million people in Metro Vancouver, so I'll never run out of people to observe.

Which brings me to one of the big reasons I wanted to write this book. I believe that history is all about observations and I think kids have a unique outlook on the world. The questions you ask are different and the answers you accept are different too. Seeing the city through the lens of a kid is one of the best ways to take a snapshot.

The stories in this collection are all snapshots in time, giving you a peek into the life of a Vancouver kid living in the past, whether thousands of years ago or just last year.

Now let me explain a couple of things. First of all, the stories in the book work forward through time, starting a long, long time ago and making their way up to this year.

Secondly, this book is a work of creative non-fiction. Maybe you know the term, or maybe you are wondering what it means. Well, here's the deal: I have searched through books, transcripts, archives, and old pictures to find stories about real kids living in Vancouver throughout this area's history. I have also interviewed lots of people about their childhood and borrowed their pictures to publish in the book. I have used my imagination to bring each true story to life, but I can promise you that I stick to the facts as I know them. At the end of each story, you will find a little section called *What do we know for sure?* There, I will tell you exactly what parts of the story are facts and what details are imagined, and I will tell you how I found the story.

I have worked hard to track down the most up-to-date and accurate information for this book. I have tried my best to find the correct contemporary spellings of First Nations names for people and places—one of my toughest challenges in writing this book.

Let's say you read something here that you want to find out more about. Maybe you want to investigate your neighbourhood or your own family history. There are lots of ways to get in touch with the history of the Vancouver area. Most of the municipalities around Vancouver have their own museums and archives. Many of these places offer great programs for kids. Don't be afraid to just go in, browse, look at old pictures, and ask questions. If you want the feeling of stepping back in time, visit places like Fort Langley, Burnaby Village Museum, or Roedde House. The Museum of Vancouver and the Museum of Anthropology at the University of British Columbia can offer you more information than you could absorb in a lifetime, but I urge you to give them a try. Check out the website vancouverhistory.ca. It is an incredible resource spearheaded by the late Vancouver historian Chuck Davis. Get creative. Go to the public library, walk around the city, ask questions of the people around you and read the little plaques attached to the sides of old buildings. You can also look on the *Courageous Kids* website, courageouskids.ca, to see a Vancouver timeline and additional information that I couldn't squeeze into this book. Take the stories you uncover and use your imagination to make them come alive. Wherever you are sitting right now is a part of someone else's story. Look around you and imagine.

Kids have been living on this land for thousands of years, but as a city, Vancouver turns one hundred and twenty-five years old in 2011. When you look at the history of the cities of the world, Vancouver is still a kid—full of adventure, energy, and courage. There have been growing pains, hard lessons, and lots of changes in the past century and a quarter. The city's story is still unfolding.

Who are you, I wonder? Are you a Vancouver kid? Did you come here on a trip? Or maybe you are planning a visit to Vancouver? Since I wrote this book, and you are reading it, we are both a part of the story. You and I are Vancouver kids when we find ourselves between these pages. I hope you enjoy the book.

Lesley McKnight
Vancouver, 2011

The Two Sisters mountains.

The Two Sisters

An unknown girl and her cousins
in Squamish territory, in ancient times

Tiny hairs on the back of my neck tickled. They stood up on end. They twitched. I stopped walking and looked around me.

I was carrying the basket of roots my mother had asked me to collect. It had taken me longer than I'd thought to find them. The sun was low in the sky and the forest was dark. I squinted through the trees. I couldn't see anything, but I heard a strange rustling in the bushes.

Sometimes the little hairs on my neck noticed things that I didn't. I had learned to pay attention to them. One time, the little hairs warned me about a mother black bear close by with her two cubs. When I stopped to look around, she passed me with her babies walking behind her. A mother with cubs can be dangerous, but I wasn't moving and she saw no threat in little me.

This time it didn't sound like an animal in the bushes.

"Who is there?" I shouted to the trees. My voice echoed. The sun dipped further and I wanted to get back to my mother.

The rustling continued, then the sound of giggles. That was no animal.

"Stop fooling," I yelled.

Two of my little boy cousins burst out of the trees, waving pointed sticks and shouting.

"We are Stek'in. We are here to take you away with us, girl," said one cousin, pointing his stick at me. The two boys jumped around hollering. They were both younger than me, smaller than me, and much sillier than me.

I ignored them and started walking again. They followed a few steps behind me, carrying on with their game.

"It's no use, you are ours now," they shouted. "You won't see your people again!" I kept walking.

Suddenly, the point of one of their sticks poked into my back. I could tell by their sudden silence that it was an accident, and it hadn't really hurt, but I'd had enough. I stopped and turned around to face my would-be captors.

"Don't you know the story of Sch'ich'iyúy, the Two Sisters?" I asked. "The Stek'in would not behave like you two beasts."

The boys looked down. They knew they had gone too far. They weren't warriors anymore and I wasn't their prisoner. I was their older cousin and they were in trouble.

"I don't have time to waste standing here. Come and walk with me. I will tell you the story again, so that you can see how silly you are being."

I set out again, glancing behind me to see that the little boys were following. They had dropped their sticks and they ran to walk beside me and listen.

"You are right that the Stek'in were once our enemy," I began. "In the past, they would steal away our women and children, but not anymore. Once, long ago, the twin sons of a highly respected Stek'in chief came here in a raid. They were young and it was their first raid so the warriors told them to stay with the canoe while they went to watch the Squamish village they planned to attack. They wanted the boys to stay safe, but the boys were like you. They didn't want to wait by the canoe. They wanted to be part of the action, so they decided to see the Squamish village for themselves. They set out alone.

8

"When they reached a ridge overlooking the village, they stopped. They spotted two Squamish girls walk out of a longhouse. It was first thing in the morning. The girls walked to the river to bathe. The twin brothers watched the girls and decided then and there that they wanted these two girls for their wives.

"The twins ran off to find the raiding party to tell them they wanted no harm to come to these two girls when they raided the village. They explained to the warriors which longhouse the girls lived in and got them to promise to protect them. The twins were the sons of the chief, so the lead warrior had to agree.

"The raid was a success. When it was over, the warriors brought the captured girls to the twin brothers. The sons of the chief were surprised when they saw the girls up close, because they were also twins.

"The twin girls were taken to the Stek'in village. At first, the girls were terrified that they would be mistreated and enslaved, but the opposite was true. They were cared for with kindness and respect. They married the twin sons of the chief and were happy.

"Only one thing made them sad. They missed their Squamish family. Sometimes, the sisters would cry, and when the Stek'in asked them why, they told them it was because they wanted their people to know how happy they were and how well they had been treated by their husbands' family.

"The twin brothers went to their father and asked him to make peace with the Squamish. The twin sisters had so impressed the chief that he agreed. The chief, his sons, and the twin sisters sent word to the Squamish offering peace. It was accepted.

"Since then, there has been peace with the Stek'in. The twin sisters lived a long life. When they passed away, the Creator changed them into twin mountain peaks so that we could always look at them and remember the peace they brought to our land.

"So little cousins, you are not Stek'in warriors. You are silly boys who need to run ahead and tell my mother I am not far behind with these roots," I told them.

Without another word, they sprinted away. I could hear them giggling again when they thought they were out of earshot.

The story had made the walk pass quickly. I'd heard it from our elders many times, but I had never said it out loud. Another hundred steps or so and I was on a ridge overlooking my own village. I looked down and saw the fires burning. I could see the little boys running to my mother to tell her I was close to home. I could see my longhouse filled with family.

I looked up to the mountains. The Two Sisters were standing guard in the mountains. They were brave girls to make a new life in a faraway place. I was happy that the twin sisters had brought peace to our people, because I never wanted my way of life to change.

I walked down from the ridge towards my village.

What we know for sure?

Have you ever noticed the two peaks that stand guard over Vancouver? Sometimes they are called the Lions. I think they look like a pair of ears poking out from behind the mountains. To the Squamish Nation, they are known as the Two Sisters.

The First Nations of British Columbia have called this land their home for thousands and thousands of years. The

Musqueam, the Lil'wat, Tseil-Waututh, and the Squamish Nation all have territorial land in what is now the Vancouver area. "Stek'in," mentioned in this story, is the Squamish word for the Haida, who come from farther north, around the Queen Charlotte Islands.

I set this story in the Squamish Nation. The Squamish Nation is made up of descendents of the Coast Salish people. In 1923, sixteen different local tribes united to form the Squamish Band.

The very first story in this book offered a special challenge. Before contact with Europeans in the nineteenth century, there was no written history of the First Nations of BC. Instead of a written history, First Nations have an oral tradition, which means that the stories and legends of their culture are passed from generation to generation through speech. Since I couldn't go through a history book or look in the archives to find a story about a First Nations kid from before European contact, I wanted to include a legend that had been passed down through time in the oral tradition.

The legend that the young girl tells her mischievous younger cousins is based on a version of the Two Sisters from a beautiful book called *People of the Land: Legends of the Four Host First Nations*. It was shared by a Squamish elder.

The southwest coast of the land that is now Canada was one of the most populous areas of early First Nations settlement. The land provided a wonderful way of life, thanks to the mild climate and the bountiful supply of food available. The ocean offered an amazing array of nourishing fish, shellfish, and sea mammals, and the land provided animals, birds, and more than one hundred and thirty different edible plants.

The young girl in this story stands on the ridge above her village and thinks about how difficult it would be to adapt to a new culture like the two sisters in the legend did. When Europeans came to her area, the cultural devastation was beyond anything she could have imagined and yet her culture thrives to this day. If you would like to find out more about the way of life the First Nations people enjoyed before European contact, there are lots of places to explore and many fantastic books to read, including the one I just mentioned.

If you were born into another culture, one way to experience First Nations culture locally is to visit the Squamish Lil'wat Cultural Centre in Squamish. There you can tour exhibits, see artifacts, and enjoy art. You can also take a guided tour, try your hand at drumming, or even make a traditional craft. Most of all, you can ask questions, which is the very best way to gain a better understanding of any culture. Check the website to see what they offer: slcc.ca.

Why I Loathe Captain Vancouver

Thomas Pitt, age sixteen
Burrard Inlet, June 23, 1792

We left the HMS *Discovery* behind us, anchored offshore in deep water many miles to the south. We had been out for days in the smaller boats that we used to navigate shallow and uncharted water. I was in the smaller yawl, under sail but not moving quickly. The crew was happy to be out exploring the secrets of the inlets and beaches.

Well, most of the crew was happy. Not I.

So why was I here? Back in England, I had craved a good adventure. This exploration of the west coast of North America had sounded to me like a bold plan. I dreamed about sailing under the British flag, claiming foreign lands for our King George. The wild landscape and the unusual people we encountered in every sea we ventured through—well, it all entranced me.

One aspect of this journey displeased me, and one alone. It soured the whole experience.

My displeasure centered on one man, one wretched and disrespectful tyrant. In the very core of my soul, I hated him. I had the great misfortune to call this man my captain. Captain George Vancouver; the name itself tasted like vomit on my tongue.

Who was he to speak to me as he did? He could command me to do his bidding, issue me orders, and punish me solely because he had the obnoxious title of captain. Yet I was nobility. I was a true son of the aristocracy. I was the son of Baron Camelford, for goodness sake! And who was Vancouver? A nothing. A nobody.

His name will be forgotten, while mine will take its place in the history of the kingdom. Any other place than on this ship, I would be able to ignore him as the worthless low-born slug that he was. But on the HMS *Discovery* he was my master.

In spite of myself, in spite of the many warnings I had received, I found myself doing things to bait the wretch. I wanted nothing more than to make Vancouver's life as miserable as he made mine. Today, it was sneaking a bit of an extra ration; I helped myself to some biscuit.

I spend my time with Charles Stuart, who is also sixteen. Like me, he comes from a noble family and therefore is a worthy companion. Charles alone understands my disgust with Vancouver. Sadly, he doesn't share my hatred of the man.

"Thomas, you shall find yourself flogged again for such behaviour," Charles said to me. He had a mischievous twinkle in his eye. "And you shall get me skinned with you."

"Vancouver wouldn't dare," I told him. "The lashing I gave him with my tongue after that flogging ensures that he shan't try it again."

"Which flogging?" laughed Charles. "The first, the second, or the third? And I think you will find his willingness to see you bleed has increased."

The knowledge that I had been whipped three times by that peasant made my skin crawl. The indignity. The outrage!

The first flogging had been ridiculous. I had taken a piece of a broken barrel hoop to trade with the natives on some god-forsaken island. Captain Vancouver accused me of having stolen it. Why would one steal something broken? He called me a thief; I called him a liar. I was flogged.

The second time was nearly the same. I traded with the natives without permission from my captain. Flogged again.

The third time, Charles and I were skylarking, climbing up the rigging of the ship for sport. As we horsed about, I fell and cracked the glass on the binnacle. Flogged again. Each time Vancouver lashed my bare back with his whip, I hardened my heart against the scoundrel.

"He is our captain, Thomas," said Charles. "I think you may have hurt more than helped with your harsh words. Perhaps a truce is in order."

"Never," I spat. "My truce will come from my grave."

"Which is precisely where our captain may wish to put you, Thomas," Charles said with a laugh. He shoved another biscuit into his mouth. As usual, Charles and I enjoy the same activities, but my sharp tongue and snide expressions get me flogged, while he receives no punishment. I, at least, have my dignity.

■ ■ ■

Suddenly, I heard a ruckus. Anxious to see the cause of such commotion, we hastily put away the biscuits and went to investigate.

All over the rigging, men were training their spyglasses on something in the distance. I followed with my own eyes, and glimpsed canoes on the horizon. We had earlier come around a big land point, named Grey by my captain, into the body of water that Vancouver had earlier named for his nephew, Sir Harry Burrard. We then passed through a narrows, catching our first sight of the large body of water beyond it. Here we saw the canoes travelling quickly to cross our path. At least fifty canoeists paddled each one.

"They seem peaceful in their mannerisms," Captain Vancouver said after looking through the telescope. "Let them approach."

One small bit of praise I can offer Vancouver is for his bravery when dealing with untested strangers, even when outnumbered. I have witnessed his courage many times on this voyage. He assumes there is no harm intended, quite remarkable since he saw his own Captain Cook murdered by just such a group in his youth. Perhaps it is not bravery; it may just be that he is not intelligent enough to judge the risk.

We were mostly silent awaiting our meeting with the men in the canoes.

"I see no European items or people in their boats," said Vancouver. "I suspect they have not met Europeans before."

As we found out, they had no English language either. We made hand signals to the strangers. We gestured the direction from which we had come and they pointed towards their village. One man handed a parcel of prepared fish over to us as a welcome gift. We had not had much success with our seine nets. We offered an array of trinkets. The men wisely chose some iron pieces over the less useful copper we presented.

The local men made a fuss over the colour of our skins, pointing to our cheeks and noses. This confirmed Vancouver's guess that we were the first Europeans to arrive. For the next couple of hours, the natives accompanied us on our journey up the channel of water. By the time we made landfall to camp for the night, there were only four canoes left, the rest having departed. We all went ashore together. We found a harsh landscape, steep with cliffs and much growth. The channel was narrow here, with the opposite shore close.

The strangers examined our belongings and we looked over theirs. They showed much curiosity.

"Ah, a musket," Vancouver said, in answer to the natives who were pointing to our firearms.

I watched the captain pick up a musket to demonstrate.

"That is ill-advised," I said to Charles. I was keeping my distance. Vancouver heard me. He shot me a hard look. I glared back.

"Point it," said Vancouver, raising the musket to his shoulder. "And, shoot." He pulled the trigger. What a fool.

The shot rang out. The men on the shore jumped, startled by the sound. They appeared shaken.

"Try it," Vancouver offered. He gestured to the group of men, who were still visibly disturbed by the demonstration.

"Another brilliant idea from our captain," I said to Charles. "Give the strange natives our firearms. Why not point them right at our heads?"

Vancouver stopped and stared at me. He said nothing for a moment.

"Pitt," he began, "we come here because we are curious about the world beyond our seas. Why not offer the gift of knowledge to those we meet? Are you so ungenerous?"

"It is not generosity you show, sir," I told him. "It is ignorance. What is to stop them from turning the trigger on us? I would not put my crew at risk if I were captain."

"Thank the heavens you are not," sighed Vancouver. "Watch your tongue, Pitt."

Vancouver handed the weapon to the nearest man and showed him how to shoot it. The young fellow was so afraid of the weapon that he trembled as he accepted it. What a foolish lesson to teach. Our captain made gestures to show that we would now make camp for the night. The native men prepared to leave, giving signs that they would bring more fish in the morning. This, at least, was welcome. The canoes cleared out.

"We shall sleep on the boat," Vancouver said. "We don't know these shores, or these tides. It is narrow here."

"I prefer to sleep ashore," I said, before thinking. Had he said we would sleep ashore, I would have desired the boat for the night. I was so sick of taking orders from this spineless jellyfish that I would make my own choices wherever possible.

"As you wish, Pitt," said Vancouver.

I gathered three others with me, all the younger crew members, and we stayed on the beach while the others returned to the yawl. As the sky grew dark, we lay down on the stones at the foot of the cliffs.

"Isn't this better than swaying all night, lads?" I asked my fellow crew members. "We spend enough time on the waves that a solid ground is welcome, is it not?"

"It is, Thomas," said Charles. "But I suspect it is not the beach you wanted. You only wished to disobey."

I finally fell asleep, though I found the stones a less than ideal bed.

■ ■ ■

I woke up with a start, cold and wet. The moon offered the smallest glimmer of light. As my eyes adjusted to the darkness, I realized the tide had come up the beach to soak us to the skin.

Two of the others sat up in a hurry. My young friend Robert Pigot bellowed at me. Can you believe that he blamed me for our rude awakening?

"Pitt, I am going to catch my death of a cold!"

Dripping with salt water, Edward Roberts shouted at me too. "I say, this is too much!"

The three of us looked to Charles, but found that although he was close to completely wet, he hadn't yet come to life. Waves lapped around his head but he was sound asleep. His legs were actually floating. I went over to shake him. He came to his senses with a jolt.

"Pitt, you fiend! Whatever are you doing . . . ?" Charles scrambled up the beach and realized what had happened. "Ah, Thomas, your wilful ways have led us astray again, I see."

We four sat on the beach, drenched and miserable, until first light. Once the sun cracked the horizon, Vancouver himself left his boat to find us huddled on the shore.

"Ha! You pups have had a nasty morning, I see."

"Bad luck," mumbled Charles, his teeth chattering.

"No, not bad luck," said Vancouver, looking pointedly at me, "I had a good chuckle as I shut my eyes last night, wondering when you would get wet. Next time lads, check the high tide line when choosing a bed. Ha!"

I looked at the captain's smug expression, and I cursed him with every nasty word in my vocabulary. Silently, of course.

You'll pay for laughing at me, Vancouver. That's a promise. You may be in control of me while we're at sea, but back home in England it will be a different story. The Vancouver name will be destroyed.

What do we know for sure?

The young sailor Thomas Pitt did eventually make his captain pay for his firm actions, but it took years.

The facts of this story are true. We know all about them because Captain George Vancouver, who gave his name to the city, kept a detailed logbook of his explorations of the Pacific Northwest. I was reading this journal in my research when I realized that some of the sailors on his ship were kids. It wasn't unusual to have boys and very young men serve on seagoing ships in Vancouver's day. Today, we have laws that prevent children from working, but those laws didn't exist then.

The captain's logbooks are a great mix of adventure and history, and if you are interested in how many places in our province received their English names, you can find the stories in *The Voyage of George Vancouver 1791–1795*.

The HMS *Discovery* left England in 1791 with another ship, the HMS *Chatham*. There were one hundred and fifty-three people on the ships, including all of the people named in this story. The English sailors set out to do three things: negotiate territories with the Spanish on Vancouver Island, then called Nootka; map the western coast of North America; and attempt to find a Northwest Passage between the Atlantic and Pacific Oceans.

In the story, Captain Vancouver's ship meets Tsleil-Wautt people in the waters between First Narrows and Second Narrows. To imagine the scene, think about present-day Vancouver. First Narrows is where Lions Gate Bridge now stands; Second Narrows is where the Ironworkers Memorial Bridge crosses into North Vancouver. The location of the camp that night is thought to be just south of Belcarra, on the opposite shore, by Dollarton Highway in North Vancouver.

In his journal, George Vancouver wrote about meeting the Tsleil-Wautt canoes, trading goods, and receiving fish. He also described how he demonstrated the use of a musket and made a note of how frightened the strangers were to shoot it.

Vancouver also recorded the funny incident of the younger crew sleeping on the beach that night and getting soaked by the incoming tide.

Nine days after this story ends, Vancouver encountered two Spanish explorers off the coast of Point Grey—Captain Malaspina and Captain Galiano—on his thirty-fifth birthday. Though he was upset to find that they had mapped more land than he had, he worked with them for nearly a month to chart more territory.

Vancouver's voyage on the *Discovery* would last for another three years, but Thomas Pitt didn't make it through the whole trip. He caused trouble throughout the journey. As the son of a Baron and the cousin of the Prime Minister of England, he disliked taking orders from a man he considered beneath him. Vancouver was forced to take extreme measures to deal with Pitt's misbehaviour, which created some controversy amongst the crew.

Finally, Vancouver decided that he'd had enough of Pitt. He dismissed him from the ship and sent him home two years early on a supply ship from Hawaii in 1793.

That is not the end of the story, however. Pitt's father died while the young man was on his way home to England, and he inherited his father's title. At home, the new Baron Camelford used his power to start a campaign against Vancouver. He accused him of being too strict with the men under his command. He said Vancouver was a poor leader. The nobleman's harsh words had ruined Captain Vancouver's reputation by the time he returned to his country.

The end of the story is quite sad. After destroying Vancouver's reputation, Camelford challenged his old captain to a duel. The encounter didn't happen, but Vancouver died less than three years later with his career in ruins. He was only forty years old.

Thomas Pitt met his own bad end, though. He died at the age of twenty-eight after challenging someone else to a duel.

Thomas Pitt had his revenge, but he was wrong about one thing: George Vancouver's name did not die with him. When the city was incorporated in 1886, it took the name Vancouver. It is thanks to his journey on the HMS *Discovery* that you are Vancouver kids today. That's better than Camelford kids, right?

Child Bride

Kw'exiliya, later known as Madeline Deighton, age twelve
Granville Township, later known as Gastown, Vancouver, 1871

The water lapped up against the side of the canoe. I loved that sound. I tapped out the rhythm on my leg with my hand. On the other leg, I tapped each stroke of the paddles. Keeping the two beats straight was hard, but I needed a distraction. It stopped me from thinking about where I was going and how much I would miss my family.

Each time the paddles dipped and pulled, I moved farther from my home. I was Sḵwxwú7mesh. I was travelling across the water, away from my people and towards my new husband. Wife. I was a wife. I had a husband. The English words sounded so strange on my tongue.

"Husband, husband, husband, husband," I repeated in time to waves and canoe strokes.

"What are you saying?" asked one of my cousins.

"Nothing," I said quickly. I could feel a blush of embarrassment travel up my face and settle in my cheeks. Such a silly girl I was being. No wife acts that way, I scolded myself.

"Jack Deighton is a good man, a good husband for you," my father had said when he put me in the canoe this morning. My aunt told him so. She knew. She was married to the stranger before me, but she died.

When she knew she was very sick, my aunt had told her husband that she would find a new wife for him. She promised him me.

I cried when my father told me I was leaving our longhouse

to go to Granville, and I begged him to change his mind.

"Why can't I marry a younger man here at home? Why do I have to go?"

He didn't answer me.

Now I was travelling forward in the canoe, slipping through the mist to my new husband. As we paddled closer to the shore, the mist thinned. Standing onshore was a big man. He looked old. He had hair on his face, all around his mouth and on his chin. His eyes looked kind, but I could see that he ate too much. The mist cleared as we drifted to shore. I could see the man smiling as he walked down the dock to meet us. This was my husband, "Gassy" Jack Deighton.

■　■　■

The first days at Granville were hard. Jack called me Madeline, not Kw'exiliya, my true name. In some ways I liked this because I was a different person here, so I should have a different name. But sometimes I thought about the way my mother's mouth looked when she said Kw'exiliya and I felt sad. When Jack's furry mouth called me Madeline, I didn't feel so good.

Jack took me home to Deighton House. It was the noisiest place I had ever been! In the daytime, men lay about on the verandah. They argued loudly and laughed even louder. Inside was worse. In the games room, men play billiards and cards all day. In the saloon, they drank all night. Shouting to each other in deep voices, they stumbled and stomped up the stairs to the rooms where they slept. I could hear their heavy boots on the stairs at all hours. How could I sleep?

I did not like Deighton House.

"You need to get used it, my girl," my husband told me when I talked to him about it.

"It's hard," I told him.

"Business is good," he said. "There are people about the area, and that's good too. They bring us money, Madeline."

"It is not the people I mind," I said. "It's their noise."

"People make noise, Maddie. They can't help that," he said.

"In the longhouse, we also had many people living together. It wasn't so loud."

"I guess they weren't having such a good time," my husband laughed.

How would he know? He knew nothing about us. My husband laughed often when I complained about life in Deighton House. I told him many times that I didn't like it and he told me many times that he couldn't change it.

In the daytime, it was not so bad. I kept myself busy with my work. But when I finished my chores, I would sneak away into the woods behind the house for a long walk by myself. I picked up dry leaves and crinkled them in my ears, trying to fill my head with forest sounds. I called to the birds and they called back. I gathered acorns and chestnuts and put them in my room in a little bowl lined with moss. I sniffed them when I felt lonely for the way things used to be.

At nighttime it wasn't so easy. I lay in my bed and tried to close my ears to the men's roars downstairs. Why can we close our eyes and our mouths but not our ears? I tried everything. I buried my head under my pillow. I sang my mother's songs to myself. I wore my bonnet over my whole head. Nothing worked.

Then one day, Jack took me out to the yard. In the corner, he pointed to a little cabin. I had seen the cabin before, but I had never been inside. Jack opened the door.

"Your new home, my lady," he said.

He had filled the room with wooden furniture: a handmade bed; a small, neat dresser; and a table with a vase filled with wildflowers. There were lace curtains on the window. I looked at Jack and his pleased expression. His eyes were dancing. He was happy with himself and happy for me.

I walked inside and sat on the small chair beside the window. I touched the curtains with my fingertips. Closing my eyes, I listened.

"I can't hear any noise at all," I said with my eyes still shut.

"Just me saying 'You're welcome,'" laughed Jack. His big voice boomed through the little cabin.

"Thank you," I said, sharing my smile with him.

"I'll leave you in peace," Jack said.

I always found Jack loud, but in the cabin his voice sounded like a shout. He got his nickname, Gassy Jack, from how much he talked. When I was near the saloon, I could always hear his voice above all the others, as he bellowed out stories from his gold rush days. Already, I had heard his most exciting tales a couple of times each. So had most of his saloon patrons, but they mostly listened happily.

I stood up from my chair and looked out the window as Jack walked towards the hotel. When he reached the door, he turned to look back. Seeing me in the window, he waved. I waved too. Then I drew the curtains, lay down on the floor and closed my eyes once again. Silence.

■ ■ ■

A week later, moonlight streamed through my little window as I lay in bed trying to sleep. At nighttime, the noise from the saloon and hotel carried farther than during the day. From the saloon, I heard the tinny notes of the old, out-of-tune piano and shouts from overexcited customers. Loud protests, such as "I've caught salmon that was bigger than you, little man!" would lead to fights breaking out and Jack's voice rising above the ruckus trying to stop the flying fists.

I stretched out my ears, challenging them to hear sounds of nature buried behind the noise of the men. "Hoo, hoo, hoo," an owl called from the forest behind my cabin. I opened my eyes. Was the owl talking to me? His hoot sounded like an invitation. I threw off my blankets and swung my feet over the edge of the bed. I sat for a moment and told myself that if he called me again before I could count to ten, I would go to him.

"One, two, three, four, five, six . . ." I counted.

"Hoo, hoo, hoo," interrupted the owl.

Quickly, I slipped on my shoes and wrapped a shawl around my shoulders. I opened the door and cut across the small patch of garden into the forest.

The trees swayed all around me, groaning as the branches moved with the wind. Big cedar boughs swept through the night sky. My eyes adjusted to the darkness. I breathed in the smells of moss, fungus, cedar, pine, and the musky scent of the animals. Nighttime creatures were a-foot and a-wing all around me.

I am not a girl who is afraid of the night. I walked and walked, deep into the woods. I had left Madeline behind. I felt like Kw'exiliya again.

"Hoo, hoo, hoo," I called to my owl friend.

"Hoo," he answered.

I wondered how strong his wings might be.

"Can you carry me away?" I called out to the owl in my own language. "Can you fly me home?"

The owl landed on a branch and looked down at me with his calm, round eyes. His eyes told me that he couldn't carry me away. They told me to stay here.

Wrapping my shawl all around me, I curled up on the soft forest floor. I made a pillow of moss and tucked it under my head. Staring up through a canopy of trees at the night sky, I saw the moon winking at me. I listened to the wind's lullaby.

I fell asleep.

What do we know for sure?

Gassy Jack Deighton, who was married to Kw'exiliya while he was in his forties, is the reason we have an area called Gastown in Vancouver today. The neighbourhood was named after Jack because he was one of the earliest and most colourful residents of Granville, the little town that grew around Hastings Mill. The owners of the mill didn't allow any alcohol on the worksite, so Gassy Jack, seeing a great business opportunity, decided to open a saloon as close to it as possible. Other tavern owners followed his lead, and soon, the town of Granville was born.

Jack was born in 1830 in Hull, England. He was an adventurer from the start, heading to sea at age fourteen. He ended up in British Columbia on a quest for gold during the Cariboo Gold Rush, but he was a better businessman than prospector. You can visit a statue of Gassy Jack very close to the original location of his saloon and hotel in present day Gastown. The original buildings burned down in the Great Fire of 1886.

Today marriage between a twelve-year-old girl and an adult man is illegal, but back when Kw'exiliya was a child it was an everyday practice in many places around the world. In that era, many people died at an early age and many women died in childbirth. Children were expected to grow up quickly, and take their place in the adult world. Many young girls were married to older European men at this time.

There is more information available about Kw'exiliya's life than most other girls in her position because she was married to such a colourful and historically significant man. She appears in all the books about Gassy Jack, a well-researched and well-documented Vancouver pioneer. I found her story in the book *Vancouver's Old-Time Scoundrels: Gassy Jack's Exploits and Other Skulduggery* by Jill Foran. Even though Gassy Jack's life was eventful and adventurous, I found myself far more interested in his young bride. I tried to imagine what her life might have been like.

We know that Gassy Jack allowed Kw'exiliya to move into the cabin at the back of the hotel property after she complained about the noise level in the main building, but there is some disagreement among historians about whether Gassy Jack allowed to her to leave as often as she did. We know that she frequently left the cabin, and, Jack for extended periods of time. Apparently, Jack had to go and find her to bring her back many times. What we don't know for sure is why she left. She usually took the furniture from the cabin with her and Jack complained to friends that he had to refurnish the cabin each time she returned. He always found her, he said, but he never got the furniture back with her. We don't know what she did with the furniture or with her time while she was away.

Within a year of marriage, Kw'exiliya and Jack had a baby son named Richard Mason Deighton, named after Jack's father and brother. The little boy grew up to be a wildly popular kid in the community, nicknamed the Earl of Granville. Everyone loved to play with the child, and cuddle him.

Pleased with the success of his business, Jack invited a brother and his wife to come and live at Deighton House in 1873, and manage the tavern. Tom and Emma Deighton weren't ideally suited to their new life in Granville. Emma had spent much of her life as a housewife in England so she needed time to get used to the wild life at Deighton House. She wasn't willing to tolerate some things, and one of them was Jack's child bride and son. The Deightons sent Kw'exiliya back to her people with baby Richard in her arms while Emma took control of Deighton House.

Jack accepted the couple's changes until 1874 when Emma organized and held a religious missionary meeting in the saloon. Jack realized that he had lost control of Deighton House. He gave it up to Tom and Emma, went off to find Kw'exiliya and Richard, and then left for New Westminster where he piloted a riverboat called the *Onward*.

Within a couple of months, news travelled to New Westminster that Emma was telling unflattering stories about Jack all over Granville. Furious with his sister-in-law, Jack returned to Deighton House to confront her. They had a huge fight. According to the story, Emma broke every piece of china in the hotel as she threw it at Jack. She and Tom left Granville for Victoria and never spoke to Jack again.

Kw'exiliya must have been happy to see her sister-in-law disappear, but her problems didn't end with Emma's departure. Less than a year later, Gassy Jack died at age forty-four after a short undiagnosed illness. A lively character throughout his lifetime, he could be loud and obnoxious, but also generous and kind.

Kw'exiliya was still a teenager when her husband died. Deighton House was sold to pay off debts and the rest of the money went to four-year-old Richard. Kw'exiliya only had enough of this remaining cash to buy her son a pair of new boots, some clothes, and a bit of candy. More sadness followed. Six months later, little Richard Deighton also died and Granville lost its favourite little Earl.

Kw'exiliya returned to the life she had known before marrying Jack. She lived on the reserve in North Vancouver until 1948, when she died at the age of ninety years old. Vancouverites knew her by her English name, Madeline. Throughout her life, she had only good things to say about her husband of five years, Gassy Jack Deighton, founding father of Vancouver's Gastown.

Can you imagine leaving behind your life and getting married at twelve years old? Kw'exiliya was a brave girl. While Gassy Jack's name is famous, hers isn't. Do you think that is fair? I'm not so sure. Maybe Gastown should add a Kw'exiliya Square.

Story Blankets

Elizabeth Silvey, age twelve
Vancouver, 1879

I helped my stepmother, Lucy, pack up our things. It wasn't easy to put away my mother's belongings. I didn't like to see them packed up in the big trunk. They needed to breathe and live out in the open, even if my mother could not.

When our mother died, her clothes, blankets, and baskets were all that my sister Josephine and I had left to remember her. Sometimes I wrapped the blankets around me, pretending the wool folds were my mother's arms. Sometimes Josie fell asleep with a corner of a blanket tucked into her closed fist.

Smoothing out my mother's old dresses with care, I packed them away in the trunk. My stepmother looked at me with love in her eyes. She understood that it was not easy to leave this place.

"Will our new house be big?" I asked Lucy.

"I don't know, Elizabeth. Ask your father."

I had moved before, but never so far. I was four when my mother died. Father was so sad, he packed up the house he had shared with her in Gastown and moved here, close to Xwá.ýxway. I missed the house in Gastown, but I returned often because Father kept his saloon next door. Outside the saloon, I could sit on the same step I had shared with my mother and think of her. I wish I could travel back in time to hold her hand.

Now my father had sold the saloon and the house in Xwá.ýxway and we were packing up our belongings again, piece by piece. We were moving to Reid Island, a two-day ride on the *Morning Star*, the sloop I had helped my father to build. I'd held the boards onto the frame of the boat for him and handed him the nails to hammer. Maybe if I had known that this boat would carry me away from all my memories, I wouldn't have been so eager to help him.

My little sister came over to the steadily growing pile of cloth and sat down next to me. She leaned her head against my shoulder.

"Tell me another story," she said.

Poor Josephine. She was only one when our mother died. She had no memories of her own, only the ones I could give her. No matter how many times I told her tales of our adventures, no matter how hard I tried to describe the way our mother's skin smelled, like the soap she made herself, they were only stories for Josephine. Lucy was a mother to Josephine in a way that she couldn't be for me. I had another mother and I would belong to her forever. As much as I cared for Lucy, she could not replace her.

■ ■ ■

"This blanket was a part of our parents' wedding," I told Josephine. I patted a thick, striped blanket that lay across my lap. Josephine stroked it gently.

"On the canoe?" she asked.

"Yes. Our mother, Khaltinaht, was an important woman. She was the granddaughter of Chief Capilano. Father met her at Musqueam where she lived with her grandmother's people."

"Was she beautiful?" asked my little sister. I had told her this story dozens and dozens of times. It was never often enough.

"Father told me that she was a pretty girl. Her shining black hair fell to the middle of her back. She had soft brown eyes. She looked very much like our aunt, Lumtinaht," I said.

"How did they marry? Tell me again."

"Mother and Father were out together alone in a canoe when he decided he wanted her for his wife. Afterwards, Father went to our great-grandfather, Chief Capilano, and asked if Mother could be his wife. He had to ask with his hands, using sign language, because he didn't speak Mother's language and the chief didn't speak English. The old chief used hand signs to say that they could be together. He motioned with his right arm and waved, quickly, upward and outward.

"They married under traditional law. Chief Capilano took our father and the chief of the Musqueam took our mother. Then the two chiefs joined them together in marriage. Dozens of canoes pulled up on the beach with many people. Relatives had collected a lot of gifts for the festivities, a big potlatch. They gave it all away, decorated blankets and such. Then they made mother and father sit in a great big canoe on top of a pile of blankets, including this one, and relatives paddled with them to their new home. And that is how they were married in those days."

"Did you see it, Elizabeth?" asked Josephine.

"No, silly goat. I wasn't born yet."

"I like that story," she sighed.

"I do too," I said. I continued to fold the blankets, lost in my own thoughts. In my head, I could see the paddles swinging together, the canoe taking my parents to their new home. Like all the tales I told Josephine, the story of my parents' marriage was nothing more than the words my father had shared with me. Yet in my imagination, his words became clear pictures. I wanted our mother to be alive for my sister. For me too.

I could see Josephine's chin beginning to quiver. I pulled her a little closer and picked up another blanket from the pile.

"This blanket has another story to tell you," I said.

"What is it?" she asked, looking up at me. The distraction had worked.

■   ■   ■

"When I was four, just before you were born, mother took me to a potlatch in the Xwá.ýxway longhouse. Back then we still lived in Gastown. Mama and our Auntie brought me over in a canoe because we were very special guests."

"Oh, a potlatch," said Josephine. Her tears had disappeared.

"Josie, you have never been to a potlatch like this one," I told her. "It was bigger than any other. I was so excited to go, but I was just little. I didn't know what to expect. Mother packed me up on her back. Our aunt was the most important young woman at all the potlatches, here or at Musqueam. Before the potlatch started, they would pile up all the blankets and sit the girl with the highest status on top of the pile. This was the seat of honour and it always belonged to Lumtinaht.

"When we got there, I think I saw thousands of people, more people than I had ever seen in one place before. It was dark inside the longhouse, and crowded. A warm fire made the room hot and smoky. The platforms were built up high inside and people were dancing. The chiefs sat way up on the platforms, throwing down the blankets and money to the guests.

"I got scared, Josie. I was so frightened that I ran away! All around me were tall legs of older people, so I darted through the legs as fast as I could to escape. I raced out of the building. I didn't wait for anyone, even Mother. She came after me. She held me to her chest, and stopped my tears. I think she wanted to stay but instead she had to take me home. I wish I could go back there now and be with Mother and celebrate the potlatch."

Josie had her head in my lap. I stroked her hair just like I remembered our mother doing.

"This blanket is from that potlatch, Josie. Mother brought it home."

"I wish I remembered her, Elizabeth," Josie whispered.

"She loved you, Josephine," I told her.

"How do you know?"

"I saw her face on the day you were born," I said.

"Our relatives took me away for a while when Mother felt ready to give birth to you," I continued. "Father was away whaling. There was no way to get word to him. I was worried, but I was excited too. I wasn't allowed to come back until the next day. I was scared to come inside the door when Mrs. Smith brought me back. Then I saw you lying on the bed. A little baby. Mother was sitting up and she looked happy and beautiful. She called me over to the bed and told me your name was Josephine."

"What did you do next?" my sister asked.

"I came to the bed and tried to yank you off! I wanted you to walk with me like a doll. Mrs. Smith and Mrs. Trim and Mother stopped me from pulling you off the bed. They were laughing. They told me you couldn't walk, not yet. I was so disappointed."

"Mother was happy," sighed Josephine. "Happy with me."

"So happy, little sister."

"Why did she have to go?" asked Josie.

"She didn't want to leave us. She got a cold in her back, father told me. You were still tiny. She asked father to send her body back to her own people when she died, and he did. She died in Gastown and the Musqueam came for her body. They took her home by canoe. She left her home in a canoe to marry father and she returned the same way."

Josie and I sat together for a little while. We didn't talk.

"When the blankets are here," she finally said, "it feels like she is here too."

I told her that she could ask me for another story anytime she wanted. She nodded.

I left Josie with her nose buried in a blanket and went back to packing.

What do we know for sure?

When Elizabeth Silvey's mother died, she was four years old and her sister wasn't yet one year old. Her father, known as Portuguese Joe Silvey, remarried quickly, partly so he would have a woman's help to care for his two young daughters. Elizabeth's stepmother, Lucy, would give birth to nine more children in the family. Historians know a lot about Elizabeth's life because she told her story to someone who wrote it down. When she grew up, she spent hours describing her life in early Vancouver to the city's first archivist, Major James Skitt Matthews. Major Matthews collected the social history of Vancouver for decades, starting in 1924. He was able to talk to some of the earliest settlers in Vancouver and ask them questions about the city's beginnings. Major Matthews interviewed Elizabeth more than two dozen times.

In her book, *The Remarkable Adventures of Portuguese Joe Silvey*, Jean Barman described Major Matthews' technique. "He would read the text back to her for any changes or additions and she would then sign the transcript with a shaky hand." He then took the transcripts, combined them with sketches from his subjects, and bound them into a series of volumes. You can ask to see them at the City of Vancouver Archives, which is close to the Vancouver Planetarium at Vanier Point in Kitsilano. I was nervous to touch those old books. They are so fragile and precious. I was worried I could hurt them. Some sections even have Major Matthews' handwritten notes. I love reading about history in the words of those who lived it. Elizabeth Silvey's description of darting between the legs of adults to escape the potlatch is so much more interesting to me than an inventory of the gifts given away by the chiefs.

The author Jean Barman uses a different spelling for the family's home at Xwá.ýxway, spelling it Whoi Whoi.

Most of the words that Elizabeth speaks to her sister in the story are almost unchanged from transcripts of her conversations with Major Matthews. She was trying to make her mother come alive for her sister in the story, but she in reality, she was also using her words to paint a vivid picture for Major Matthews of a time when newly married couples paddled off to their new lives by canoe and potlatches were the biggest social events of the season.

Elizabeth and her brothers and sisters had Portuguese and First Nations ancestry. Many of the second generation of Vancouverites were born to First Nations mothers and fathers with European heritage. These children were equally comfortable in both cultures, and they thrived in a rapidly changing community. Elizabeth, for instance, spoke Portuguese, Chinook, Cowichan, and English.

In the story, Elizabeth is preparing to move with her family to Reid Island, which lies between the much larger islands of Galiano and Thetis. Compared to busy, growing Vancouver, Reid Island must have felt remote and rugged for Elizabeth. Her father built a new house, carefully winding an old grapevine around the windows. He told his daughter that the plant had come with him all the way from Portugal.

Elizabeth's life took an unusual turn in 1883 when she was sixteen years old. She had been seeing a young man named James Walker, but both she and her father had told him that she was too young to be married. James didn't want to wait for Elizabeth to turn twenty, as her father had instructed. Instead, he asked her to take a ride in his rowboat. As soon as she stepped in, he rowed Elizabeth to Kuper Island and married her against her will. Later in life, she spoke with regret about marrying so young. She had ten children with James, four of them before she was twenty years old.

Elizabeth returned to Vancouver without her husband after the First World War. She took a room in a boarding house on Cambie Street, where she lived out the remainder of her years. One of her greatest pleasures once she returned to Vancouver was getting in touch with Madeline Deighton, Gassy Jack's wife from the last story in this book. She went to visit Madeline on the Squamish Nation's Mission Reserve in North Vancouver and was thrilled to discover that Madeline remembered her as a little girl.

Elizabeth died in 1945 at the age of seventy-eight. Thanks to the work of Major Matthews, and the city historians who followed him, you can read about her life in this book.

Survivors gathered around temporary shelters after the
Great Fire, including children. Maybe they are the Irvings?

Vancouver is Burning!

A daughter in the Irving family, age unknown
Vancouver, June 13, 1886

My brother pinched the tender skin on the back of my arm as hard as he possibly could for the fifth time in a single day. "That's the last time," I screamed, running after him. Mother had already scolded me once that afternoon for fighting back when he pinched. I tried to explain to her that he'd hurt me. As usual, I was the one who got the lecture. She didn't even listen to me.

"Your brother is smaller than you are," she told me.

"And meaner," I uttered under my breath.

Mother frowned at me but pretended not to hear. "Practise kindness and try to be ladylike," she said.

Kindness to that brat??? What a ridiculous idea! Every second Mother turned her back, the kid gave me a new bruise. And why should I be ladylike in a rough place like Vancouver? I see nothing too civilized about this place. If Mother and Father were forcing us to live in this wilderness, why couldn't I behave like a wild creature?

I grabbed for my brother's arm, but missed. As he sprinted away, he ran backwards so he could make a nasty face at me while he made his escape. I could see a huge exposed tree root coming up behind him. "Ha," I shouted. "I don't have to catch you. That tree will get you for me!"

He looked confused for a second and started to turn around, but it was too late. The root tripped up his feet and he crashed to the ground.

"You're horrible," he yelled.

"Don't be a goose, it was the tree that made you fall," I protested. I worried that Mother would hear him crying.

His tears were just beginning to flow when my mother came hurrying towards the back garden from the front of the house. My brother's hands were scraped. I was going to get a tongue-lashing.

"Children, come here this instant!" Mother shouted. I braced myself for the scolding that was sure to follow, but something about my mother's face stopped me. She wasn't angry. She was scared.

"The city is on fire," she said. "Men are running up and down the street telling people to run." I ran for the house, but mother stopped me. "There is no time to get anything," she said. I thought of my treasures inside the house—my doll, arrowhead collection, the photograph of my grandmother in Seattle.

"What about Father?"

"He's working by the water, which is exactly where we need to be." The three of us ran for our lives.

■ ■ ■

As soon as we left our back garden, I realized Mother had good reason to be frightened. Even full-grown men were running down the road, which scared me to see. I could smell smoke and I tasted ash on my tongue. Looking back over my shoulder, I glanced up Carrall Street. The summer sky behind us was filling quickly with thick, black smoke. Each second that passed, the sky grew darker. Only a few minutes after leaving our yard, it felt as dark as night, though it was the middle of the afternoon.

Only it wasn't like nighttime. A strange, orange glow followed us. The air grew warmer and warmer. An odd sound surrounded my mother, my brother, and me. I heard a constant roar underneath the shouts and cries of the people around us, and it was getting louder. It was the fire eating the city.

"Mother," I cried. "Mother, where are we going? Where is it safe?"

She didn't answer. I had the terrible feeling that she didn't respond because she didn't know herself. My mother was uncertain about which direction to head. She hesitated. Finally, she started running blindly with us in tow. Any direction was better than standing still and waiting for the fire to consume us.

My little brother stumbled, and Mother and I looked behind us as we pulled him up. Flames, bright orange and yellow, chased us faster than we could run. Buildings on both sides of the street at the end of the block were completely engulfed in fire. Wooden boardwalks alongside the road were burning too. The air wasn't warm any longer; it was hot.

"Mother . . ." I choked. Smoke and fear caught in my throat. My mother's eyes met mine and we both looked down at my brother's face, now dirty with tear tracks from the soot and crying.

"Try to cover your mouths and noses with your clothes," shouted Mother. "This way!" She pulled us down a path towards the water. It was cooler there, quieter too. Now, I couldn't hear the shouting people on the run, only the fire.

Mother let go of our hands and ran ahead to see what the end of the path looked like. For a moment, my brother and I stood frozen and apart. Smoke surrounded us. He stared at me from above the handkerchief he was holding over his mouth and nose. I saw how scared he was. Looking at him, Mother's words went through my head. He was smaller than me. I reached out my hand and he grabbed it. He squeezed next to me and held my entire arm close to the side of his body.

"No good," gasped Mother, running back towards us. "Go back," she said, struggling to talk through the smoke.

We turned around, running back towards Carrall Street. Every step we took, it got hotter. By the time we reached the road, we were breathing air as hot as cinders. The scene before us was madness. I could hear a church bell ringing frantically in the distance. Terrified people ran down the road with their clothes on fire. A wall of fire stretched in every direction.

As we stood there, I thought about all the houses and stores that had once lined the street, about our house and our belongings inside it. I thought about my father and wondered where he was, if he was safe. I hoped he was safer than we were.

"What are you doing?" asked a man running past us on the street.

"We're . . . trapped," sputtered my mother. I knew she was right. My heart jumped in my chest. I squeezed my brother's hand even tighter.

The stranger grabbed my mother's arm and pulled us all along behind him. He was sprinting and we struggled to keep up. We ran all the way to the end of Carrall Street.

"There's only fire," I yelled. "Where can we go?"

"We'll run through!" Is that what the stranger shouted? It was hard to hear him above the roar of the flames, but I refused to believe that was his plan. I looked to my mother and she nodded. I let go of my brother's hand and hooked his arm through mine instead.

We all took a deep breath and ran.

■ ■ ■

We broke though the wall of flames, and came out unburned on the other side of the fire. I couldn't believe we made it.

My relief lasted for a split second. We had made our way to the water, but there was no safety there. Dozens of people stood on different docks along the waterfront, struggling to get into any boat available. I saw some canoes and one big coal hulk taking on people, but there was no help where we stood.

"We can't swim," my mother shouted to the stranger.

The stranger yelled to the men in the boats. "Over here! Help us. There are women and children!"

No one seemed to hear our calls. My mother was starting to panic as the flames behind us crept closer. The heat was becoming unbearable.

"Should I throw them in the water?" she asked the stranger. "I would rather see them drown than burn."

Them? Was she talking about us? Only minutes earlier, I had laughed to see my little brother hurt. Now, more than anything, I wanted to protect him.

The three of us huddled together, turning our faces from the heat. As I looked into the water, I saw the reflection of the flames around my face. It seemed as if the ocean itself were alight.

I heard my mother gasp. Could it get any worse, I wondered? I looked up to see a canoe pulling alongside us.

"We're alright," I whispered to my little brother as I leaned down to hug him. "We're alright now."

What do we know for sure?

I came across the story about the Irving family, consisting of a mother and two children, when I was reading about the fire in the City of Vancouver Archives. It was frustrating, because I saw anecdotal reports of the Irvings in a couple of places, but I couldn't find the name of the witnesses or anything else about the family, including the two children's names. I wanted to know more about those brave kids and what happened to them later.

An unnamed man interviewed after the blaze talked about rescuing the family when he came across them as he was escaping. I tried to research more about the Irving family, but couldn't find out any more about them. Instead, I imagined what it would have been like for two small children to experience Vancouver's most terrible fire. The witness reported that Mrs. Irving was panicking right before their rescue. He said that she talked about throwing her children into the water just as a canoe pulled up to save them.

When the fire began on June 13, 1886, Vancouver was only two months old. The town of Granville, which Elizabeth Silvey described in the last story, had been declared the new city of Vancouver on April 6, 1886. Can you imagine how frustrated and upset residents were when most of the city burned to ash only eight weeks later?

The Great Fire of 1886 was devastating. In only forty-five minutes, hundreds of buildings and numerous lives were lost. The fire started partly because city developers were in such a big hurry to make the city grow. People wanted to move to Vancouver and they needed houses to live in, and buildings for businesses. Thousands of huge trees surrounded the city. The fastest way to get the trees out of the way was to cut them down and then burn them where they fell. Workers set fires all the time, clearing the land for new Vancouverites.

On that Sunday, they began a controlled burn on the Canadian Pacific Railway land to the south of town to clear trees and underbrush around present-day Pender Street. When the wind unexpectedly shifted from northwest to southwest, the fire moved towards the city. At noon, the fire was under control, but by two o'clock most of the city's buildings were burning or destroyed. By five, the fire had burned itself out. The danger was over and the damage was done.

All that remained standing in Vancouver were a brick hotel, a small fish oil refinery, a brewery, and Hastings Mill. The city's early pioneers had worked hard to build Vancouver but most of the residents of the city were left with nothing after the fire. They had the clothes on their backs and little else. Most were just happy to be alive.

The best estimate is that twenty-nine people died in the fire. One of the saddest discoveries was a woman and child found at the bottom of a well. They had been safe hiding in the well until the fire passed overtop of them and they suffocated. At one point, the fire was thought to have caused thirty deaths. A Vancouver doctor, Dr. H.E. Langis, overheard a searcher describing a victim he had found. Only the skeleton was left behind, he heard, but the poor fellow's bones were all wired together. The doctor asked a few more questions about where the body had been discovered. It turned out that the "victim" was actually the anatomical skeleton Dr. Langis kept in his office.

The ringing church bell in the story is real. It belonged to St. James Church, at the corner of Cordova and Gore streets. The minister risked his own life to ring the bell and alert the city to the threat of the fire. His actions saved hundreds of lives. He escaped, but the church burned to the ground. The heat of the flames melted the bell into a misshapen lump. If you want to see what is left of the bell that saved so many, you can find it in the Vancouver Museum.

Many Vancouverites escaped the fire by canoe. When the fire broke out, the flames and smoke were visible from the North Shore. When the Squamish First Nations communities saw the disaster unfolding, they manned as many canoes as they could and paddled to the rescue. A huge iron-hulled sailing ship anchored in the harbor, the *Robert Kerr*, also rescued dozens of people who would have otherwise died in the fire.

Survivors gathered at Hastings Mill and in tents made from blankets at False Creek. Although the residents of Vancouver were devastated by the loss of their city, they were determined to not let the fire destroy their optimism. By lunchtime the very next day, the first wagonload of fresh lumber arrived at the still-smoldering fire site. By dinnertime, hammers were banging and saws were singing. The rebuilding of Vancouver had begun.

The Intruders

August Jack Khatsahlano, age eight
Chaythoos, 1887

"Chulwalsh, Chulwalsh, Chulwalsh . . ."

I listened hard for the sound of the bull. I didn't hear him.

"Chulwalsh!"

I had to feed the bull before I could go inside and eat my breakfast. I was hungry. I thought the bull was probably hungry too. I wanted him to hurry up and get his breakfast, so I could get mine.

I could hear some thrashing in the trees, but deep in the woods. Maybe I needed to call louder. I opened my mouth to shout but then heard a rustle coming from behind me. I turned around and saw the bull walk out the bushes on the other side of the garden, not where I expected him. Not where I thought I'd heard him.

Chulwalsh and twelve cows help our family. My mother takes their milk by canoe to Hastings Mill, to sell to the workers there. My sister Louisa makes butter out of the milk and my mother sells that too.

My father died five years ago, when I was three years old. Now his body lies in his own little house. It is only a short distance from here. It sits high on posts made of cedar trees. It has windows all around. I can look inside and see his coffin, covered in a red blanket. He is always nearby, close to his family.

It was one of the cows that killed my father. A cow kicked him in the head while he was milking her. He bumped his head on the wooden wall of the cow stall. Sometimes I wonder which cow killed my father. I wonder if she knows what she did.

Now my mother and my sister Agnes milk the cows. One

time I asked Agnes if it scares her. She didn't say anything. Maybe she didn't hear me. Or maybe she didn't want to say she was scared.

"Good bull, Chulwalsh," I said. I touched his giant leg. So strong and powerful.

Time for breakfast.

■ ■ ■

I was hungry. Food was the first thing I thought of when I woke up in the morning. I always think it is funny that I get up early every morning to feed our eight pigs, our two horses, and Chulwalsh the bull, but I have to wait to eat. Once my work is done, I want to be fed too.

We don't eat what the newcomers eat. I have heard of their bacon but I can't imagine eating a pig. We sell the meat from our cows and pigs, but we don't eat it. We eat deer, clams, fish, duck. No beef. No pig. Some foods the white man brought to us taste good. I like turnips and potatoes. We grow them ourselves now.

"When I go to deliver milk, I want you to dig the garden, make it bigger on the forest side," my mother said to me as I took a bite of bannock. I only nodded. There is always work to be done. I liked to tend the animals and the garden, but I have one sadness inside that I never tell anyone about, not even my brother or sisters. My secret wish is to go to school.

I often see other children go by canoe to the school at Hastings Mill. They carry books. They are learning to read and write. I want to be able to do those things too.

When the cow kicked my father in the head, she took school away from me. With no father here, I need to help.

"Later, I will go get herring," I said.

"Carefully," said my mother.

I didn't know what she meant. I wasn't sure if she wanted me to be safe, or if she wanted me to be more careful with the fish. A few weeks earlier, my brother and I went fish-raking and got lots of herring but on our way home, a strong tide tipped over our canoe. We lost all the fish but I was almost lost too. I held onto the canoe as hard as I could. We went back and got more herring, but we didn't catch as many the second time. My mother was disappointed because we need lots of fish. She dries them on sticks in the hot sun. We eat the herring in wintertime when there isn't as much food.

"I am careful," I said. "I keep . . ." Suddenly, an odd sound interrupted me.

Clunk. Clunk. Clunk.

Our house rattled.

"What was that?" asked my sister, Agnes.

"It sounds like someone chopping a tree, but our house is the tree," said my mother. We all stood up and started to move towards the door.

Clunk. Clunk. Clunk.

A cup at the edge of our table tumbled off and hit the ground with a crash. The whole house vibrated with each blow. We all bolted outside to see what was making the noise.

Two white men were standing next to our house. They were talking, but I didn't understand what they were saying because they spoke quickly and only to each other. One man had an axe. He raised it up and swung it down.

Clunk. Clunk. Clunk.

He was chopping the corner of our house! Huge chunks of wood were flying everywhere. I realized with a jolt that the noise in the distant bush that I'd mistakenly thought was Chulwalsh this morning, was actually these two men.

"Ask what they are doing," my mother said to my sister Louisa. Louisa is much older than me. She was the only one who spoke English well. She was married to a white man, Jim Burns. She walked over to the two men, who seemed surprised to see her.

"Why are you chopping at our house?" she asked.

"We're making a road," said the man with the axe.

"Whose road?" asked Louisa. "The white man's road?"

"We were told to make a road around the whole place," said the axe man.

They kept talking for a little while, but they used too many big words I didn't know. Then Louisa came back to the rest of us as we stood in the doorway of our house. The man with the axe resumed chopping at the corner of the building.

"They said that they have to build a road and our house is in the way," she said.

"What?" asked my mother.

"I am not sure," said Louisa. "He said they made this a park. He said that the road will go through our place, but that we will get lots of money."

"I don't want money," said my mother. "I want them to stop chopping down our house. They didn't ask. They didn't knock on the door."

"He said they only need to take away the corner," said Louisa. "For the survey line." She said these last two words in

English. She shrugged, because the term didn't make any more sense to her than it did to my mother. There was nothing we could do but stand aside and watch the axe man chop away at our house.

I tried one more thing. I wished with all my power that Chulwalsh would come storming out of the brush. The sight of a huge, terrifying bull would surely drive these men away.

I waited, but Chulwalsh didn't come.

What do we know for sure?

Can you imagine having your breakfast interrupted by people chopping down your house unannounced? In 1897, August Jack and his family lived in a small house inside the tall woods when a construction crew arrived to turn their lives upside down.

Stanley Park is one of the most popular landmarks in Vancouver today, but it wasn't always a park. The City of Vancouver created Stanley Park on June 7, 1887. At that time, Vancouverites were busy rebuilding the city after the huge fire the year before. The city was growing and Vancouver City Council was working hard to create all sorts of new city features, including parks.

I found out about August Jack's story in the book, *Stanley Park's Secrets: The Forgotten Families of Whoi Whoi, Kanaka Ranch and Brockton Point* by Jean Barman. In the book, the author argues firmly for recognition of the settlements that existed in Stanley Park before it was claimed by the city. "Not only were families dispossessed, the memory of them was erased," she wrote. "Only when the sites are returned to our collective memory will Stanley Park belong to all of us." I couldn't agree more.

Think about downtown today. It is packed full of high-rise office and apartment buildings. If the city hadn't created Stanley Park when it did, what do you think it would look like now? Instead of the thousands of trees, ponds, gardens, trails, beaches, and playgrounds we enjoy, Stanley Park would look the same as the rest of downtown. The big problem with creating the park, however, is that the land wasn't empty. Hundreds of people called this land their home.

Remember Xwá.ýxway, also known as Whoi Whoi, from the story of Elizabeth and the potlatch? In a few more pages you will also read about families living at Kanaka Ranch from the story about Minnie and the first CPR train. Both of those settlements were also located on the land that became Stanley Park.

August Jack's house stood in the way of the road being built around the perimeter of the park. His family lived in a village called Chaythoos, very close to what is now known as Prospect Point. If August Jack were still in his garden today, he would likely look up at the underside of the Lions Gate Bridge.

Citizens of European origin in Vancouver in the late 1800s considered the aboriginal families in Stanley Park as squatters on the property, which means that the government didn't think they had any legal right to be on the land. August Jack's family never saw any of the money that the road surveyors promised to his sister Louisa.

When August Jack's mother, Qwhaywat, learned about the plans for the road, she made a quick decision to move Supple Jack's remains out of the way of the construction. August Jack watched as his family tore down the house that was specially built for his father's blanket-draped coffin.

On September 27, 1888, the mayor of Vancouver, David Oppenheimer, left city hall with a huge procession that included a twenty-piece band. The big group arrived at the exact location where Supple Jack's grave had been. The mayor gave a speech that described the new park as "a place of recreation in the vicinity of a city where its inhabitants can spend some time amid the beauties of nature away from the busy haunts of men." He declared Stanley Park officially open.

The city hired Henry Avison as the first park ranger and he immediately set to work developing the park land. You will meet his son in a story called *The Bear that Saw Lace Underwear* on page 71.

Eventually, all of the families and individuals living in Stanley Park were forced to leave. August Jack and his family left in 1889. They moved to Sun'ahk, or Snauq, which was another Squamish settlement located right below the place where the Burrard Street Bridge stands today. That land was also eventually taken over. The residents of the village of Sun'ahk were relocated to the Squamish reserve in 1901. I read a vivid and chilling description of the relocation in Robert Budd's beautiful book, *Voices of British Columbia: Stories from our frontier*. In it, Isabel Sweeney, who was a young girl of twelve at the time, recalled watching tugboats drop off two scows for the villagers to load up with all their belongings. At high tide that same evening, the tugboats picked up the scows and pulled them away to the Squamish reserve. Isabel saw the Sun'ahk residents set the buildings they left behind on fire right before they floated away to their new home. "I can remember watching and being aware that I was watching history," Isabel said.

In 1905, the Canadian Pacific Railway took something else from August Jack: his name. The land developers were trying to sell property in a new suburb around the old village of Sun'ahk. They thought the ancestral Squamish name Khatsahlano had an historic ring to it that would help them sell real estate. Without asking permission, they altered the spelling to Kitsilano and a neighbourhood was born.

August Jack Khatsahlano didn't forget about Chaythoos or Sun'ahk. We know all about his early life because, like other kids you have met in this book, he spent many hours describing his childhood to Major Matthews when he was an adult. He talked about Chulwalsh the bull, overturning his canoe after fish-raking, and the morning that his breakfast was interrupted by an axe. He also expressed regret that his father's death prevented him from going to school, as he wished he could read and write.

August Jack came from a line of Squamish chiefs and his heritage was important to him. In fact, after a career as a longshoreman, Chief August Jack Khatsahlano returned to Stanley Park in the 1940s to sell First Nations articles at the Brockton Point souvenir and food stand. Large crowds would gather and he would enthrall tourists and park visitors by sharing legends and historical information about himself, the area, and the articles he was selling. In 1966, August Jack and his half brother Domanic Charlie wrote a book called *Squamish Legends*, in an effort to capture the stories and places of his childhood and ancestry. He died in 1967.

Hundreds of First Nations Vancouver kids had similar experiences to August Jack, watching European newcomers slowly take over the land of their ancestors. Sixteen tribes in the Vancouver area united in 1923 to form the Squamish Band. The Squamish Nation website (squamish.net) describes the process they are still going through to reclaim some of the traditional lands they lost. This land claims process involves a lot of negotiation. For example, according the Squamish website, the claims started by the Squamish nation in 1993 are, "currently at Stage Three of a Six Stage process. The late Squamish Chief Joe Mathias described the pace of these negotiations as "glacial.'"

I have spent many hours enjoying Stanley Park on my own and with my kids. I am grateful to live in a city with such a massive and magical park right downtown. I bet you have lots of happy memories in Stanley Park too. But I was sad to learn how many people, including lots of kids, lost their homes when the park was created.

Next time you are walking around the seawall, driving over the Lions Gate Bridge, or visiting the Vancouver Aquarium, take a couple of minutes to look around you and imagine the communities of Xwá.ýxway and Chaythoos long ago. Think about kids like Elizabeth Silvey, Minnie McCord, and August Jack Khatsahlano too. For us, Stanley Park is a wonderful place to visit and have fun. For those kids, the majestic forest was home.

Children and teachers at Hastings Sawmill School,
including Minnie McCord, on June 11, 1886.

That Fearsome Iron Horse

Minnie McCord, age ten
Vancouver, May 23, 1887

"I don't know if Grandmother will let us go watch the train come in," I told my sister, Seraphine.

"But Minnie," she said. "Everyone will be there."

So they would. Everyone we knew would go. The children at school had been talking of little else for days. Weeks even. The very first Canadian Pacific train would pull into Vancouver today on tracks that had crossed all of Canada to end up near our front door.

The truth was that I didn't want to welcome the locomotive to town. It was silly really, but trains frightened me. I hadn't seen one close up before, but I was sure they were noisy, dirty, and dangerous.

"I saw bands setting up to play, Minnie," said Seraphine. "I want to go. Please."

"We have to ask Grandmother," I told her. I tried to make it look like I was very busy sweeping the kitchen floor so that maybe Seraphine would lose interest and leave.

My plan didn't work. Seraphine was jumping up and down. When my sister got an idea into her head, there was no getting it out.

"Minnie, Minnie, Minnie . . . Minnie, we'll miss it." Seraphine tugged on my skirt. She yanked on my hand. Her cheeks were red with excitement.

I sighed. She wasn't going to be put off easily.

"Alright, little one, let's go ask Grandmother," I said.

Seraphine squealed with delight and ran ahead. We found Grandmother on the ground outside, picking strawberries. She had on her wide-brimmed hat, as always, so we could not see the expression on her face. Grandmother waited for Seraphine to get her question out. My sister was nearly speechless; she was so worked up with excitement.

"Grandmother, grandmother, people are already gathering. There are flags up and a band, and . . ." Seraphine tried to catch her breath. "The ladies will be dressed so beautifully. And all of our friends from school will be there. Please . . . ?"

Grandmother waited until her outburst subsided. "Minnie, you haven't said anything," she said, turning to me. "Would you like to go see the train come in?"

"It would be interesting, I suppose," I shrugged.

"You don't sound as happy as your sister, little clam," she said.

"I am," I told her. My voice was flat. Grandmother raised her eyebrows, asking me a question with her eyes. I turned to look at Seraphine. She stared at me with wide eyes. She was silently pleading with me to be excited.

Grandmother waited for a moment before turning to look at us from her spot on the ground. She had a basket full of strawberries in her hand, which she passed to me.

"Tell you what," she said. "I need someone to take these strawberries into town. You can do me a favour and drop them off at the Alexanders."

I knew what she was doing. Grandmother wasn't going to tell us that we could go, but she was sending us on an errand that would put us right next to the train when it came into town. She wasn't giving me a choice. Seraphine knew it too.

"Whoopee!" she squealed. She grabbed the basket out of my hand and started off down the path. She was making train noises and clapping her hands. I shielded my eyes from the springtime sunshine and looked at my grandmother. She winked at me. My shoulders slumped.

"History is in the making, little clam," she said. "Off you go."

■ ■ ■

I caught up to Seraphine, already well ahead of me on the path to town.

"Seraphine, you naughty thing," I told her. "There is so much we could be doing to help. Instead, we are running off and leaving Grandmother to work."

I fell into step beside my sister and took the basket out of her hand.

"Minnie, we do nothing but work and go to school," she said. "This is a tiny bit of fun."

Deep down I knew she was right. Even since my grandfather Eihu died last year, we have been working hard. The money our grandmother makes selling apples, berries, and fish to other families once provided just a bit of extra income for us. Now without Eihu's earnings, the fruit money is all we have. Our mother brings us money when she can, but she isn't around much and we can't count on her contribution.

"Seraphine, let's take the beach way," I said.

"Why?" she asked. "Are you scared?"

Sometimes I wonder why my little sister is the brave one. This was the same path we took to school every day to Hastings Mill. I often tried to get Seraphine to go on the beach path with me, even though it was longer. This path through the woods frightens me. I could see shacks in the bushes just behind the trees where runaway sailors and other men who had cause to disappear would hide. Sometimes they would jump out just to see a young girl scream. I always had the urge to run, but Seraphine sauntered along, swinging her arms without a care in the world, singing a little tune under her breath.

"No matter," I told Seraphine, trying to sound confident. "And in any case, I won't be walking to school after this year, anyway." I was partly pleased about this fact and partly sad. I had already told my grandmother that the time had come for me to leave school so I could take a job and help earn money for the family. She had agreed.

Seraphine slowed down in front of me and reached back for my hand without saying a word. I skipped ahead and grabbed it. I knew what she was trying to tell me.

■ ■ ■

We emerged from the woods to see the hustle and bustle of thrilled crowds.

"Minnie, I hear the band," Seraphine said, tugging my hand. "Let's hurry."

We were half walking, half running now. Seraphine was nearly dragging me. As we approached the crowd gathered at the foot of Granville Street, I could see a huge arch built out of evergreens. It was decorated with bunting and flags. There were hundreds of people gathered, all looking more interested than I felt, but I couldn't help a tiny twinge of curiosity brewing. Then I spotted him. Harry Alexander, my mortal enemy. He was standing next to his father, proud as a little girl with new ribbons. He thought he was so special just because his father was the Hastings Mill manager. He stood among the fancy-dressed people, preening at his reflection in the glass window of a nearby store. We were supposed to deliver my grandmother's strawberries to his house.

Harry and I had never been friends. An incident occurred when we were younger that cemented a strong dislike between us.

My father was Scottish, so that's why my last name is McCord. My mother is half Hawaiian and half Squamish and Musqueam. Every Sunday when we went to church, I dressed up in full Scottish garb: a kilt complete with a little Scottish hat called a Glengarry perched atop my carefully done curled hair. When I was younger, I was a tiny bit of a thing, smaller than other children my age. My father would carry me into the church on his shoulders. It was the happiest feeling I can imagine sitting up there, seeing the world from up high.

We'd sit all together, Seraphine, Mother, Father, and me. After church, we would go together to visit my little sister Maud's grave. She died when I was four. We would stand around the little picket fence that Father had built around her headstone and talk to her. Then we would put flowers on her grave and tell her that we missed her. Church days were my favourite family days.

One day while I was sitting on my bench in church, quiet as a mouse because the minister was talking, Harry Alexander pulled my curls as hard as he could from behind me.

"Ouch!" I screamed. Standing up, I turned around to face him. I pulled off my Glengarry hat quick as a flash and whacked him on the head with it.

I didn't think about it before I did it. It just happened. Everything stopped and the minister gave me a stare like no other. My father looked sideways at me and shook his head. Oh, he thought it was a terrible thing I had done. In church, no less. That awful Harry Alexander made me do it. I hated him for pulling my curls. And I double-hated him for making the minister and my father look at me with so much disappointment.

I glared at him now, standing so smugly between his mother and father, waiting for the train with his shiny shoes and his hair brushed neatly. He looked up and saw me.

I straightened up and held my head high. I would not let Harry Alexander see me frightened of a train. "Come on, Seraphine," I said loudly. "Let's go over there to watch." I hoped I sounded brave. I wished I felt brave.

As soon as we reached the evergreen arch, I pulled Seraphine behind the bushes so that we were out of sight of Harry Alexander.

"Let's stand here," I whispered in Seraphine's ear. "If the engine comes off the track, it won't run us over."

"Silly Minnie," my sister protested. "It won't come off the tracks. I can barely see from here."

"Just peep through the evergreens to see," I hissed.

■ ■ ■

The huge engine barrelled down the train track towards us. Steam filled the air, puffing up into the sky. The noise was deafening. The band played. The crowd cheered. Blasting boat horns in the harbour welcomed the first train to Vancouver. The train whistle hooted as the locomotive approached the station.

I was glad it was loud because my little sister couldn't hear me whimper with fear. Seraphine's hand gripped mine, but not because she was afraid. She was thrilled.

"Seraphine," I said. "Let's move a little further back. Seraphine? Step backwards. What if it comes off the track? Seraphine . . . !" She didn't hear a word I said. As I pulled back on her hand, she leaned forward to look down the railway tracks.

Engine 374—bigger than any moving thing I had ever seen—was coming straight for us! Louder and louder!

Why had I agreed to come and see this huge, smoke-belching monster? I stumbled backwards trying to escape, and knocked over the basket of strawberries that I'd placed carefully at my feet. I stepped on a bunch as I tried to regain my footing. I couldn't deliver these berries, all dusty and bruised, to the Alexanders. Grandmother wouldn't be happy.

Stepping backwards, the evergreen bough no longer blocked me from the view of the crowd. I quickly glanced over at Harry, expecting to see a smug grin on his face. He surprised me. He looked just as scared as me, or more. Our eyes met and he smiled a little bit. I smiled back.

The train pulled up in a cloud of steam and dust. It was so loud that it felt as though the train had just belched and steamed its way right into my brain. The railway had connected the two coasts of Canada. I'd survived the first train, which was more than I could say for the strawberries.

What do we know for sure?

Today, Vancouver bustles with cars, trucks, ferries, Skytrains, ships, planes, and city buses, so it is hard to understand how a train could be so scary for Minnie. In her lifetime, Vancouver was a much quieter and slower-moving place. The first train's arrival was significant in a place where the fastest, noisiest, and largest method of land transportation had been a horse and carriage.

Engine 374 arrived in Vancouver on May 23, 1887, completing the CPR's difficult construction of a rail connection for Canada, coast to coast. This massive project took ten years and the hard work and sweat of twelve thousand men to complete. No wonder, since the rail line was sixteen hundred kilometres long. The railway was a monumental achievement. Originally the line stopped in Port Moody, but the track was extended an extra ten miles to Vancouver.

It was an exciting time for the inhabitants. Vancouver was only a year old as an official city, and its citizens were rebuilding after the big fire a year earlier. People were optimistic about the bright future of their community. They were developing Stanley Park, as you read in the last story. Businesses and houses sprang up almost overnight and dozens of newcomers were arriving in the city every day. For many people in Vancouver, the arrival of the first train was a symbol of progress.

You can visit Engine 374 today. It is preserved at the Roundhouse Community Centre in Yaletown, housed in its own specially constructed pavilion, built for Expo '86.

I don't know for sure if it was Minnie's grandmother who encouraged her to go see the train that day, but I do know from reading interviews Minnie gave Major Matthews that she was nervous about going to the celebration. She told Major Matthews that she and her sister Seraphine hid behind the cedar arch because she was worried the train might jump off the track. It is also recorded that the girls' grandmother, Mary See-em-ia, was a wise and kind woman, so I imagined her gently urging the girls to go and witness history in the making. Mary often encouraged her granddaughters to observe and learn all they could about the changing world.

I imagined the interaction between Harry Alexander and Minnie that day, as well as the strawberry delivery. However, the story about Minnie's rivalry with Harry is true, as is the fact that the girls delivered fruit to neighbours for their grandmother.

Minnie's grandmother, Mary See-em-ia, saw many changes in her lifetime. She grew up in the Squamish community of the Mission Reserve in Capilano, North Vancouver. She met Minnie's grandfather, Eihu, and moved with him to Kanaka Ranch. Eihu was from Hawaii and he and other Hawaiians settled Kanaka Ranch together, exactly where the Bayshore Hotel stands today.

Minnie described her childhood at Kanaka Ranch very fondly. Thanks to her grandmother's hard work, she remembers a childhood filled with an abundance of food and love. Minnie and Seraphine's mother, Maggie, moved in and out of their lives after she remarried and started another family. The girls' grandmother was the person who offered them stability. When their grandfather Eihu died in 1886, life became a little more difficult. As Minnie hints in the story, she quit school and went to work to help support her grandmother and sister at the age of ten years old. She had to grow up very quickly.

When she was eighteen, Minnie married William Smith, who had come west from Montreal, and they raised three children.

Seraphine's story, on the other hand, had no happy ending. She was forced to attend a residential school called Coqualeetza in Chilliwack. The boarding school was intended to teach young First Nations children how to assimilate with newcomers, but most students of the residential school system came away with mental and physical scars from their time away from home. For many, the forced removal from their families and culture proved too difficult to overcome. Seraphine was no exception. After five years at Coqualeetza, Seraphine moved in with Minnie to help take care of her children, but she struggled to find her place in the world. Then in 1907, she married a Danish roofer named Jens Marstrand. One year later, she took her own life by swallowing poisonous tablets.

The new railroad represented progress for many residents of Vancouver. Minnie was anxious about the train itself, but she found happiness in the Vancouver that grew up around the railroad. Seraphine was thrilled by the excitement of the event, but ultimately she wasn't able to survive in the new world that the train brought to her home.

Henry Avison and his father outside the
Park Ranger's cottage in Stanley Park, 1896.
VANCOUVER ARCHIVES S-5-4

The Bear That Saw Lace Underwear

Henry S. Avison, age eight
Vancouver, 1898

I dipped my finger into the milk and held it out to the baby raccoon. He sniffed, then grabbed it in his mouth. His tongue was soft, but his teeth were not.

"What's in the box?" My sister Sarah leaned over my shoulder to take a look.

"Baby raccoons," I told her. "Their mother was gone. Killed, I think. So I brought them home."

Sarah watched me wincing in pain. That baby raccoon had little daggers for teeth. He was sharpening them on my finger bone. I tugged, trying to get my finger out of his mouth, but he held on tight.

"Why do you have your finger in its mouth?" asked Sarah.

"He seemed hungry, so I'm giving him milk," I said.

"He'll probably chew through your finger. Did you try giving him a bowl full, instead?"

"Of course I did, smart aleck," I said. Actually, I hadn't.

"I think you should go ask Mother. She'll know how to feed it. Maybe baby raccoons don't like cow's milk," said Sarah. I figured she was right. This baby raccoon seemed to like boy's blood. I gave a yank and pulled my finger out of his mouth.

"I asked her already. She was in a tizzy. The minister and his wife are coming for tea. She was baking and cleaning. No time for raccoon babies, she told me."

It was rare for Mother not to take an interest in the animals that my brothers and sisters brought home from our wanderings around the park. Anything we found orphaned, injured, or interesting came home with us. She could nurse almost any sick creature back to health.

My father was the park ranger for Stanley Park, but his job was all about preventing fires and stopping Vancouverites from logging the place into a wasteland. My mother, on the other hand, was trying something new. She was making a zoo. She thought it would be a marvellous way to attract families to the park. So far, it was working. For us, the best part of her dream was the fun of searching the park for new captures to add to the zoo's collection.

"I forgot about the minister and his wife coming," said Sarah. "I'd best go inside and clean up. I was playing with the ducks in Beaver Lake." She was covered in muck. I looked down. I was filthy too.

"Looking at the way Mother was attacking the kitchen floor with the brush, I think we should get clean before she sees us," I laughed. "If she scrubs us like that, I think we'll lose skin!"

■ ■ ■

I carried the milk pitcher inside and put it on the kitchen table. Mother came into the kitchen just at the moment I realized I had tracked mud across the clean floor.

"Sorry, Mother," I said. Normally, she would laugh and say never mind. Most days it was just as likely to be Mother dragging in mud as me. Not today. Today, she had opened the sideboard and pulled out the good china, brought all the way from Ireland. I had thought those cups and saucers were only for decoration. I didn't know we could actually use them. Today there had been more baking than playing, which was strange for my mother. There had been more cleaning than teaching, which was also odd.

"Mother, why is it such an important thing for the minister to come?" I asked her, as she bent down to rub at my dirty footprints.

"I don't know myself, Henry. I remember my own mother labouring to make things perfect for such visits when I was a wee girl. I believe we try to impress. We want civilized people to feel that we also are civilized, I think."

"Aren't we?" I asked.

"In our own way, Henry. In other ways, we live on the edge of a vast wilderness. As much as we try to hold back Mother Nature and her creatures, we shall never win that fight."

"Fight? But why would you fight it? I don't see you fighting, Mother. We are a part of nature, are we not? Why should we pretend otherwise?"

Mother stood up and wiped her hands on her apron. She laughed.

"You are wise, young man. I suppose you are right. Nevertheless, I have good china and it is nice to put it out. We can be a mixture of wild and tame, can we not?"

I shrugged. I rather liked wild myself.

"Henry, where are you bringing the milk in from?"

"Outside," I told her. "I was trying to feed the orphaned raccoons."

"You weren't touching the animals and sticking your fingers in the milk, were you Henry?"

My silence answered her question.

"I cannot serve raccoon milk to the minister's wife, Henry!" She sighed, looking into the pitcher.

"A touch of raccoon milk might be good for her," I said. "Perhaps she could use a drop of wild."

■ ■ ■

When the minister's wife walked into our parlour, I saw that she might need more than a drop of wild. Maybe the whole pitcher's worth.

Everything she wore was white—from her gloves to her high-heeled boots. I shouldn't wonder that she needed an hour to do up all the buttons on the boots. Imagine the things you could get done in that hour, rather than just doing up fussy-looking boots! She carried an umbrella with her, even though the sun was shining brightly, and the silly thing looked as though it wouldn't keep out the lightest of rains. It was nearly see-through. Her entire getup looked foolish in every way to me. It was fine in church perhaps, but out of place at my house.

We sat stiffly in the parlour for what seemed like hours. The adults' conversation was so dull that I ceased to listen. I told myself stories in my head while marvelling that the minister's wife could take such a long time to eat a small biscuit.

"I hear, Mrs. Avison, that you have quite a collection of animals here in the park," said the minister's wife. My ears perked up. Finally something interesting.

"Indeed," said mother. "The children and I rescue creatures that are wounded. Some we nurse to health and return to the wild. Others we keep. I have also ordered some more exotic animals. I wish to create a zoo of sorts, for families to visit."

"My wife has a wonderful way with animals," my father added.

"And children, I suppose," said the minister's wife. She

looked down her long nose at the six of us, brushed, starched, and stiff. The words she said didn't match the way she said them. She was looking at us in a way that made me feel she wasn't much impressed with the Avison clan. Well, the feeling was mutual.

"Perhaps you would like to see the animals?" my father asked the minister and his wife.

"Oh, Henry. I am not sure our guest is dressed for traipsing around the zoo," my mother said hastily.

"I should be delighted," said the minister's wife.

She didn't look delighted, but I was pleased to be heading outdoors. Maybe I could sneak away to check my raccoon babies.

■ ■ ■

"Over here is a doe that we found as a fawn," mother explained. "She was starving. We fed her and she survived. Once she was strong, I tried to set her free into the park. She kept coming back here, so we constructed a small pen for her. I suppose we're her family now."

As mother was speaking, the minister's wife held a lily-white handkerchief over her nose.

"I see," she said. "And what is this over here?"

"A kangaroo," my mother said proudly.

"A kangaroo?" echoed the minister's wife. "I had no idea we had wild kangaroos in British Columbia."

My mouth fell open and Sarah barely stifled a laugh.

My mother's eyebrow rose slightly. She paused for a moment before saying, "No indeed, not wild. This one is from Australia. It was sent over specially."

The minister's wife blushed a deep red. I let out a tiny chuckle and Mother shot me a sharply disapproving look. "Master Henry, do you have a favourite animal in the zoo?" the minister's wife asked, trying to change the subject of conversation.

I choked back my laughter. "The bear, I should think," I told her.

"Perhaps you'd like to show me," she said.

We walked towards the stump where the old bear was chained. I liked the bear, with his huge paws and the battered collar around his neck. But what I liked most about the bear was watching my mother with him.

He was big. He had a mouth full of huge, sharp teeth. When people approached him, he rose up on his hind legs and made a throaty growl that you could feel in your shoes. I found him quite terrifying. My mother, on the other hand, was a friend of this cranky old bear. She could approach him and stroke his shoulder. He'd nuzzle her with his massive snout, rubbing her side. It was like magic to me, because no one else could get near him.

"Oh," said the minister's wife. "I expected something bigger. He's quite small, really."

"I'd say he's bear-sized," my mother said.

"I suppose," said the minister's wife. "I have always felt so terrified of bears, but this one makes me think I have been silly all these years."

In my mind I silently agreed with her. She certainly seemed silly to me, and not just about bears.

The minister's wife walked closer to the bear. "You aren't so scary, are you?" she asked. In response, the bear started to rise up, a growl brewing in his throat. The minister's wife took a small step closer. "You almost look pathetic there, tied up to a tree stump. How ridiculous you are!"

With those words, the minister's wife pointed her umbrella right at the bear. Before my mother could say a word to stop her, the minister's wife poked the grumpy old bear right in the middle of his big chest with her umbrella tip.

In an instant, the bear swiped the umbrella out of her hand with his lightning quick paw. His claws ripped right through the delicate lace, pulling it to pieces in seconds. The minister's wife's instincts were all wrong. She made a move to retrieve the umbrella, stepping even closer to the angry bear.

"Stop, you mustn't!" Mother was shouting now.

It was too late. The bear saw his opportunity, dropping the umbrella to lunge at the minister's wife. His claws sank into the folds of her skirt. As she began to shriek and shout, the bear grabbed the material of her white dress and yanked at it.

We all stood by in shock as the bear ripped the minister's wife's skirt right off.

A moment earlier, she had called this powerful beast ridiculous. Now she was standing in the Vancouver sunshine in her undergarments, which I noticed were also white. She was fortunate the bear hadn't hurt her, although her feelings were certainly wounded. As she collapsed into a heap on the dirty ground and her husband rushed to her aid, I thought the bear had mastered a magnificent bit of revenge.

I couldn't hold in my laughter. It burst out of me, completely unstoppable. Luckily, the adults were too busy dealing with the situation to notice.

I started to run away, but not before I saw my mother turn

away from the minister's wife who was sobbing in the dirt. The corners of my mother's mouth were turned up. She was fighting a smile. She caught my eye and we both covered our mouths and shared a laugh.

What do we know for sure?

The bear that attacked the minister's wife escaped in the chaos. He slipped his collar over his head and ran into the woods. It wasn't the first time he'd run away. He was known for his ability to escape. Under normal circumstances, Henry's mother would venture into the forest and seek him out. She was the only one who could ever find him. For her, he would return to his chain on the stump.

This time was different. The minister and his wife raised a ruckus, demanding that the bear be destroyed. They wanted him hunted down and killed for his vicious behaviour.

Henry's mother protested. She felt the bear had been pro-voked into attack when poked by the umbrella. She won the battle and the bear was spared.

I stumbled upon the story of the ill-fated minister's wife while browsing Major Matthews' *Early Vancouver* at the Archives. In it, I found the transcript of an interview Major Matthews had with Henry Avison, in which he describes the incident. Although Henry was a grown man at the time of the interview, he recalled his recollection of the bear and the underwear with the delight of a child. I laughed out loud in the quiet archives while reading it, drawing some looks from my fellow research-ers. Unfortunately the names of the minister and his wife were not recorded.

Henry's family left the park the following year, but the zoo continued to grow. More and more animals were added over the years, until it was eventually home to more than fifty different creatures, from wolves to monkeys. Over the decades, thousands of Vancouver kids enjoyed family outings and school trips to the zoo, including Judy Bau, a girl you will meet later in this book. The animal enclosures improved in time and no animals were attached to chains on a stump, so there were no more bear paw swipes or umbrellas destroyed.

The Vancouver Aquarium was added in 1956, bringing more animals to the park population. It remains one of the most popular destinations in the city.

You cannot visit the Stanley Park zoo today. Despite the more humane conditions of the modern zoo, Vancouver's citizens began to argue over the well-being of the animals kept in captivity. A city-wide vote in 1994 made it clear that most Vancouverites wanted to see the zoo dismantled. They made only one exception for the zoo's polar bear, Tuk. It was decided that the old fellow should be permitted to live out the rest of his days in his enclosure. The last resident of the Stanley Park zoo died in 1997, marking the end of Mrs. Avison's dream.

The Avison family is remembered in the park with their own street. The Aquarium is located on Avison Way.

I think an even better way to remember the Avisons is to take part in an activity organized by the Stanley Park Ecology Society (stanleyparkecology.ca), an organization that Mrs. Avison would surely have joined wholeheartedly. You can find their Nature House at Lost Lagoon. Tell them Henry Avison sent you.

The Roedde family.

My Lucky Automobile Accident

William (Bill) August Roedde, age ten
Vancouver, 1900

"Come on, Walter," I said. "The sand is all piled up, just like the beach." I had found a most wonderful sand pile at the end of our block. I had big plans, but I needed Walter.

"I'll be there, but I have to practise piano first," Walter sighed. He pushed open the sliding door of the parlour with a frown. No boy wants to practise piano on a sunny day, especially when his brother is heading outside to play.

I am lucky to have Walter in my life. He is only a year older than me, adopted by my parents right before I was born. His mother was a German opera singer living in Vancouver. She died having him. Since my parents spoke German and my father adored opera, they brought him home.

Given Walter's musical background, Mother and Father have higher hopes for his musical talents than for mine. Too bad for him, because that means they make him practise piano more often.

I ran into the kitchen to get a pot to fill with water. I wanted to scoop tracks in the sand pile outside, then pour the water down the track. When Walter came out, we could have an opposites race. If the water took longer to reach the bottom of my track, I'd be the winner.

I grabbed the full pot out of the sink. *Crash!*

I'd knocked over the ice tongs. When they fell, they made the most awful racket. The sound of the metal crashing into the kitchen tiles was so loud it hurt my eardrums.

I froze, waiting to hear if the colossal noise had woken up my baby sister upstairs. Nothing. Thank heavens.

My other little sister, Anna, came running around the corner of the kitchen from upstairs. "Billy, Mother said . . . Mother told me that . . . she said you need to be outside to . . ."

"Spit it out, Anna," I said. Her little three-year-old brain was struggling to get out the message from the nursery, where mother was putting Tilly down to sleep. Maybe I had better make my escape before she got it all straight. I was worried that Mother's orders would include a request to take Anna outside with me. "Never mind, Anna. I'm leaving."

As I turned to go, I saw she was struggling to lift the heavy ice tongs by herself. I started to help her, but I was too late. The tongs crashed to the ground again. This time, the baby's cries started immediately. Time to make my escape.

I grabbed the pot out of the sink and started towards the front door. Tilly was wailing. Anna trailed after me, "Billy . . . Billy, Mother said . . ."

Water from the pot splashed all over the floor in the front hall. My situation was getting worse by the second. Running past the parlour door, I could hear Walter on the piano. "I'll be on the corner, Walter," I shouted on my way past.

I ran out the door, pulling it shut behind me. The wind caught it, slamming it so hard that the windows rattled. Tilly's cries in the nursery increased in volume. I could hear her out on Barclay Street.

No time to waste around here, I thought. Maybe if I disappeared for a few hours until dinner, I could avoid the worst of the trouble. With luck Anna would get a towel and wipe up the spill to help me avoid the worst of it. Mother was tiny, smaller than me even, but when she was mad, she grew huge in my imagination.

Outside, the sun was shining and the smell of sea salt was in the air. I quickly forgot my home worries and travelled to the end of the block where I had discovered the sand pile. If I practised making the tracks before Walter got there, I'd be sure to win.

I carried the water down to the corner of Barclay and Nicola and set the pot down next to the sand. Then I stuck two of my fingers in the very top of the pile. My fingers became an automobile. I revved my engines for a moment and then drove my fingers down the slope, carving a deep, curving track down the side of the hill. The auto swerved and curled, taking incredibly sharp hairpin turns.

I had only seen one automobile in my life, but the memory of it was burned into my brain. Mr. B.T. Rogers was one of the richest men in town and he'd just brought the very first automobile to Vancouver. His family made its money selling sugar. I could certainly understand how a fortune could be made in a business like that. After all, sugar was one of the only things that I bought with my own money.

Mr. Rogers loved to drive his new auto around town. I'd heard people complain that he drove too fast, but you'd never hear such a complaint out of me! If I had such a fancy machine, I'd spend all my days driving. Besides, the automobile didn't go any faster than a horse and buggy, and it was no more dangerous, I'd venture. People just weren't used to it.

The only time I'd seen Mr. Rogers' auto myself was at Stanley

Park Lake. I had taken my double-barrelled muzzle-loader gun down to the water to shoot ducks. Lying in wait for the ducks, I heard a sound that shook my insides. It was a rumbling, spluttering noise that I'd never heard before. I stuck my head out of the marsh reeds to see Mr. Rogers speeding along the wooden-pile bridge right next to me. Magic!

Without thinking, I whooped in excitement. "Woohoo!" I shouted.

Mr. Rogers turned to see me crouched by the side of the lagoon.

"Woohoo!" he shouted back. I couldn't believe it. He looked like an important man, but he sounded like a little kid. I watched until I couldn't see him or his strange contraption anymore.

Ever since that day, automobiles have appeared in most of the games that Walter and I play.

■ ■ ■

My track was ready. I scooped a handful of water with my hands and dumped it. Most of the water just soaked into the sand. Drat.

Maybe if I poured a bunch of water right from the pot.

Just as I was lifting the pot to dump the water, I heard a sound in the distance. It was the same spluttering noise I'd had in my head ever since the day I had seen Mr. Rogers at Stanley Park Lake. It must be the sound of an automobile and the racket was getting louder. It was coming this way!

I dropped the pot and ran around the corner towards the noise. I didn't want to miss my chance to see Mr. Rogers again. The sound was close and loud. I bolted onto the street.

Smash.

It was the strangest thing. Suddenly I found myself lying on my back, looking up at the sun. Then the sun was blocked by something. I squinted to recognize it. It was Mr. Rogers' face. He looked down at me, worried about what he'd just done.

"Kid, are you alright? Say something, kid. Can you talk?"

"What happened?" I asked.

"I bumped into you with my car. You came out of nowhere," said Mr. Rogers.

I tried to sit up, but my head felt funny. I lay down again.

"Oh kid," moaned Mr. Rogers. He leaned over and picked me up off the road. I looked up to see frowning people gathered on the sidewalk. "He's just dandy, folks. I'll take him home to his parents." Then he whispered to me: "Tell the people you're fine."

I waved weakly. "I'm f . . . fine," I stammered.

Mr. Rogers carried me to his automobile, which was still rumbling. He placed me gently on the front seat and walked around to the other side. He sat behind the wheel. "What's your name, son? Where do you live?" he asked.

"Billy Roedde, sir. I live on Barclay Street." Sitting in the front seat of a real automobile made me feel instantly better. I didn't want to miss a second of this ride, so I sat up straight. Mr. Rogers looked relieved.

"Let me drive you home, Billy Roedde. Your mother will want to know you are fine. Direct me to your house."

I admit I did not give Mr. Rogers the most direct route home. I took him the long way, past Nicola Street, back to Haro Street, then Broughton Street. I enjoyed every second of the adventure. Walter would be so jealous. Not only did I get to see Mr. Rogers' auto again, I was riding in it! I almost burst with excitement.

When we pulled up in front of my house, Mother came rushing out. Obviously, news of the accident had reached home before we did, because she looked anxious.

Mr. Rogers came around to my side and lifted me out of the automobile, carrying me towards my mother. "Not to worry, Mrs. Roedde. The lad seems unhurt. I only nudged him."

Walter appeared behind my mother, his mouth hanging open in shock. Mother followed Mr. Rogers as he walked with me straight up the front stairs, through the hall and into the parlour. He placed me down on the couch. Mother hurried to my side with worry all over her face. My eldest sister, also named Anna, had died before I was born. When she was five years old, she'd eaten poisonous berries. Mother tried not to fret over us, but I knew that sometimes she thought about Anna and her eyes would get wet. She had the same look on her face right now.

"I'm sorry I woke the baby, Mother," I said. I wanted her to feel better.

"Hush, Billy. Don't worry about that. You are safe. Rest now." She kissed my forehead. She and Mr. Rogers walked into the front hall, talking quietly.

"Thank you, Mr. Rogers," I said as they were leaving the room. He smiled at me, then turned back to Mother. Anna and Walter rushed into the parlour. As soon as they saw that I had survived, they began peppering me with questions about the automobile and my ride.

"Walter, Anna Catherine, out of there. Leave Billy to rest," said Mother from the front hall. Anna left, but Walter leaned down next to me. "You are so lucky," he whispered. "I wish Mr. Rogers had hit *me* with his car."

"Woohoo," I whispered. "It was worth it, alright."

What do we know for sure?
The house that Billy lived in with his family is now a museum called Roedde House in downtown Vancouver. I learned about this story when I went there to do research. You can visit the house too, and stand in the same kitchen, front hall, and parlour that appeared in this story. You can even see the ice tongs that Billy knocked over. Ice tongs were used to lift the huge blocks of ice that Victorian families needed to keep their perishable foods cool in the years before modern refrigerators were invented. The tongs are right beside the sink in the museum kitchen.

I used my imagination to provide the details of the accident Billy had with Mr. Rogers, but we know how it happened and where. He was playing in a sand pile and when he heard the sputter of the car's motor, he ran into the road to see the vehicle go past. We know that after he was returned home safely, Billy felt really lucky to have been hit by one of the first automobiles in the city. His brother Walter was jealous!

You can also see photographs of the Roedde family and examples of the things they would have used in their turn-of-the-century Vancouver house. Stepping into the house is like stepping back in time to Vancouver in the early 1900s. Can you imagine a time when the population of Vancouver was only fifteen thousand people?

One of the reasons that the Roedde House became a museum was that it was designed and built for the Roedde family by an important British Columbia architect. Francis Mawson Rattenbury is famous for designing the BC Legislature Building in Victoria. He also designed the Hotel Vancouver and the BC Courthouse, which is now the Vancouver Art Gallery. The only family home he built in Vancouver was the Roedde House, created for Gustav and Matilda Roedde in 1893.

Gustav and Matilda had come to Vancouver in 1890. Born in Germany, they lived for some time in the United States before moving to BC. Gustav was the first bookbinder in Vancouver, having learned the craft at a young age in Germany. His bookbinding business was successful and the family settled into a secure middle-class life in Vancouver. The Roeddes had six children, including their first daughter, Anna, who really did die from eating poisonous berries. Walter, their adopted son, was also raised by the Roeddes after the death of his mother, an opera singer.

Both Walter and Billy served overseas as soldiers in the First World War. If you visit Roedde House Museum, you can see the letters that the boys sent home to their family. Fortunately both young men survived to return to Vancouver and take up the family bookbinding business.

Anna Catherine wasn't as lucky. She grew up and became a nurse, but at the age of twenty-eight, she was killed by a mentally ill patient while she was working at St. Paul's Hospital. The name Anna was not a lucky one for the Roedde family and future generations avoided it.

The family sold the house not long after Anna Catherine died. It changed hands numerous times over the years and had a long stint as a rooming house. It was in a sorry and neglected state when it attracted the notice of a local history buff. A movement began to restore the home to its former glory as a West End Victorian beauty.

A visit to the Roedde House Museum is a fantastic way to get a taste of turn-of-the-century Vancouver. If you go on a Sunday, you can even enjoy a cup of tea and cookies. You can see for yourself the scorch marks in the dining room from the time the Roedde family's candle-lit Christmas tree caught on fire and nearly burned the house down. Luckily for the Roeddes, the Vancouver Fire Department's Hall 2 was right around the corner and the house was saved. You can also try standing at the tiny kitchen sink that was custom made for the tiny Mrs. Roedde, who was only four-foot-eleven.

Just don't knock over the tongs next to the kitchen sink. They make an awful racket.

House Girl

Elsie Hong, age nine
Vancouver, 1902

The steam from the tea filled my nose. It smelled flowery. I picked up the cup, my pinky finger stuck out at the side, just so. I sipped. It was delicious, but too cool. I would talk to the house girl about it. I liked my tea piping hot, no less.

I picked up a biscuit. I sniffed it, but I didn't care for its fragrance. Rather than eat it, I bent over and held it out to my little dog. His tongue darted out to lick it. He barked . . .

I sat bolt upright in my bed. What time was it? Had I overslept? I peered out the window, trying to judge the hour from the amount of light outside. Oh, no! It looked bright.

Lost in dreams again. It was bad enough that my mistress accused me of daydreaming, now I was behind in my morning routine because of nighttime dreams. At least I could try to control my wakeful wanderings, but how could I stop dreaming in my sleep?

Sipping tea and feeding little dogs. It was too ridiculous. I jumped up and quickly dressed. I was late. I could feel it.

If my mistress woke up and felt the chill in the air, I would catch a world of trouble. If she so much as cracked one eye open, she would know that no fire had been lit.

I scrambled to the stove and got to work. Before lighting the fire, I needed to rake out the coal ashes from the day before. Heaven help me if it made a sound.

Hurry, hurry, hurry, I said inside my head. In my haste, I banged the metal handle of the broom against the fire grate.

Clang.

I waited. Luckily I heard nothing but silence upstairs.

I quickly swept the rest of the ash and laid out a fresh fire. As soon as I lit the firewood and felt the air warm up around me, my shoulders relaxed. At least the fire was going. Maybe it would be all right.

Yip Yen's second wife, my mistress, was short-tempered and exacting. In the two years I had been working here, not once had I ever received a word of praise. The greatest encouragement I ever got was the absence of anger. If she wasn't actively yelling, I assumed she was pleased.

Sometimes I wondered how things would have been different in another household. When I was brought to Vancouver from China, I was told I would live in Yip Yen's household, but not where. I heard that other employers were more patient. Some even let the servants attend school. Girls I knew who worked in Yip Sang's house went to school for hours every day. I couldn't even imagine. I didn't have spare hours every day; I didn't have spare minutes.

Besides, who would waste time filling a house girl's head with knowledge? You don't pour valuable wine into a worthless jug, or so some people said. It would be a waste.

A shadow passed across the floor at my feet. I jumped.

"You are lazy," said my mistress in her clipped, flat tone.

Yip Yen's second wife moved like a ghost. I never heard her coming.

"I am sorry, mistress," I said.

"I heard you bashing around in the stove, you clumsy girl," she said.

"I am sorry, mistress, very sorry," I muttered.

"You were late getting up also," she said. "You think I don't notice, but I do."

And didn't I know it? She noticed everything.

"You think only of yourself," she scolded. "You don't think of me trying to sleep. You are a noisy girl on purpose."

Think only of myself? I spend every hour of my day thinking only of her, trying to anticipate what she needed before she yelled at me. Think only of myself? Think what, I wondered? What would I think, if I were to think about myself?

I had no idea.

"I am very sorry, mistress," I said again.

"I will take my breakfast in bed," she told me. She glanced at the stove. "Ach," she groaned. It was a special sound she made in the back of her throat, saved just for me. Pure irritation. "You haven't even put on the water, yet. You are a useless thing. I would be better off doing it myself."

I didn't believe that. She wouldn't be better off doing it herself, because I didn't think she was capable. I had never seen her lift a finger, except to put food in her mouth.

"I will do it, mistress. Right away," I said, my head bowed.

She was gone. I filled the kettle and placed it on the stove, dreading the clatter that accompanied it. I covered a yawn with the back of my hand.

■ ■ ■

It was Tuesday, the day I scrubbed all the floors in the house. This was one of the worst days of the week since I had to lug heavy buckets of scalding, soapy water through all the rooms. By the end of the day, I felt like my arms were two inches longer. I could almost feel my bones stretching from the weight of the buckets.

I had knobby knees, which my mistress pointed out to me often, telling me I was scrawny and weak. My bony knees ached after I'd bent down on hardwood floors all day. I never could tell if the red, chafed skin on my knees was from the floor or the boiling water I knelt in to scrub.

After tossing the last of the dirty water out the kitchen door, I thought about the chores I had left to complete. I sat down on the ground to rub a bit of pork fat into my poor knees.

"Have you nothing better to do than sit around?" snapped a voice behind me. I scrambled to my feet and shoved the little pot of pork fat under the stove with my foot. My mistress had just appeared out of nowhere, as usual. "I must find more for you to do, for idle girls cause trouble. I'll have more sewing work brought by for you. I cannot abide laziness."

Normally I enjoyed talking back to my mistress inside my head. I imagined all the things I would say if I weren't afraid of her. Today I was too tired. Her furious words washed over me and my mind was blank.

"The rice this afternoon was mushy," she said. "It is remarkable that you can ruin rice so consistently. I suppose everyone has a special talent." She shrugged. "Oh, and you didn't come to my bedroom to retrieve my coffee cup this morning. It spilled off my dressing table just now, all over my nicest gloves. I have to wear my second-best gloves to Jung Kee's for dominos. You shall have to scrub the gloves and rewash my floor. Finish last week's sewing when you are done, and no sloppiness this time."

My hands were so red and chapped from the hot water and

soap that it would be painful to sew tonight. Never mind, I still had at least an hour's worth of work to redo the floors in the mistress's room.

She sashayed out the door without a backward glance.

I put more water on to boil.

■ ■ ■

Finally, I was finished. After the extra hour of scrubbing the bedroom floor for a second time today, I was nearly craving my sewing work. At least I could sit down to do it. My mistress hadn't yet figured out a way for me to clean and sew at the same time—though trust her to try.

I knew that Yip Yen's second wife made good money from my sewing because I was an excellent seamstress. My stitches were tiny and even. I had even heard women guests in the house talking about my sewing, though passing on the words of praise to me would never happen. Kind words would surely stick in my mistress's throat and choke her.

There was still work to be done before sewing, however, and I was running behind. I hurried to scoop up my rags, brush, and bucket, careful not to slosh the dirty water. I needed to get downstairs quickly.

I rushed down the hallway. My arms felt like lead weights, they were so tired and heavy. I reached the stairs, but in my haste, I caught the toe of my boot under the carpet runner than ran down the middle of the stairs.

I felt myself falling, but I was desperate to prevent the filthy water from spilling down the entire flight of stairs. I twisted to keep the bucket steady, but instead, lost my footing completely.

The world was spinning. I could feel the brush tumbling down the stairs beside me. Water was everywhere, soaking me and the carpet until we were drenched. I tried to stop myself, but couldn't. I tried to put my leg out against the wall, but the momentum couldn't be stopped. My ankle gave way and I rolled down the rest of the stairs.

I landed in a heap at the bottom of the stairs. I suppressed tears and tried to get up. If I didn't clean up this mess before my mistress returned home, I might as well throw myself into the stove to save her the trouble. Sharp, searing pain shot up my leg. It was blinding. My vision sank inward like a shrinking circle of light. Everything went black.

■ ■ ■

For two weeks after my fall down the stairs, I limped around on a leg that felt like it was on fire.

My mistress had arrived home to find me sopping up the water at the bottom of the staircase. She barely looked at me. Dominos had not gone well. The next morning, I woke up with an ankle twice its normal size. It was throbbing and aching, but there was nothing to do but get up and pretend all was well. As the days passed and my limp worsened, my mistress would occasionally remark upon how slow I was to work, how long it took for her breakfast to reach her bedroom, or how unsightly my walking was. I apologized every time.

Then one day, Jung Kee came to the mistress's house for dominos. I carried in the tea tray, but every one of my uneven steps made the teacups clatter against one another.

"What's wrong with your girl?" asked the lady Jung Kee.

"Oh, well, she's lazy, argumentative, and foul-tempered," began my mistress.

"No," said Jung Kee. "Why does she walk like a broken doll? I think she is hurt."

"What? What do you mean? Oh that, she's been like that for . . ." my mistress suddenly stopped. "Oh my, she is limping. Oh dear. Elsie, whatever have you done? Have you injured yourself?"

I didn't speak.

"She needs a doctor," said Jung Kee. "Look at the size of her ankle. She can't even lace her boots properly. What have you done to yourself, girl?"

Before I could answer, my mistress spoke for me.

"It must have been from your fall this morning, Elsie," she said. "Was it?" Yip Yen's second wife shot me a look that told me to play along with her lie. "You poor thing," she said, her eyes cold, but her face shaped into concern. "I'll call for a doctor this instant."

Jung Kee looked at me. Her eyes rested on me for some time before she turned back to my mistress.

"A doctor, right away," she said.

■ ■ ■

My mistress removed my boots and arranged me on a settee. Until that day I had never been permitted to touch it, except for dusting. Now I was laid out on it, as though I were some kind of empress. I had blankets tucked up to my chin and a pillow behind my head.

As soon as Dr. Munroe arrived, Yip Yen's second wife began fussing around me as if she was the servant and I was the mistress.

I had a glass of tea and second pillow under my leg, hand fluffed. "Now, let's have a look," said Dr. Munroe in English, as he knelt at my feet. He lifted the blanket and peered at my leg. He looked up at me, his brow furrowed.

"How did you injure yourself?" he asked me.

I did not know what to tell him. I had heard my mistress tell Jung Kee that it had happened that morning, not two weeks ago. If I told the truth, I made my mistress a liar. I said nothing.

"She fell this morning," said my mistress. "She's a clumsy girl."

Dr. Munroe touched my leg causing me to flinch and cry out. "Hmmm, this is not a new injury," he said. "It's badly infected. Over a couple of weeks, I'd suggest. Not good at all." He stood up and faced my mistress. "She's been walking around on a broken ankle," he said. Dr. Munroe and Jung Kee looked at my mistress, who blushed a deep red. "She's clumsy, as I said. And deceitful too. She no doubt hurt herself, then hid it from me."

"She is a talented disguise-artist then," said Dr. Munroe. "It would not be easy to walk around on such a severe break, while the infection spread up her leg." He and Jung Kee exchanged glances. "Well," he went on, "it will cost her dearly. The foot is poisoned because the bone was not set after the break. My recommendation is amputation."

Before I could stop myself, I blurted out, "Amputation?" I did not know that English word. Everyone ignored me.

"You cannot cut off her foot," said my mistress.

Cut off my foot?

"How would she work? Who will marry a girl with one leg? It's out of the question," said Yip Yen's second wife.

My mind was racing. I knew that my ability to work was first and foremost on my mistress's mind, but for once, I did not mind. Without a leg, I was useless to her. How would I get up the stairs in the morning with her breakfast? Hopping? I shuddered.

"I strongly suggest amputation," repeated Dr. Munroe. "The girl could die."

"She might as well die if she has no foot," said my mistress. "She will have no future with one leg."

"Are you certain?" asked the doctor.

"Let her be," said Yip Yen's second wife. "If she lives, she lives."

For once, I agreed with my mistress.

What do we know for sure?

I will set your mind at ease right away and tell you that Elsie survived her infection. She kept both her feet and grew up to marry Earnest Yet.

Today an infection like Elsie's would be treated with antibiotics, but that medicine didn't exist in 1902. Her condition was very dangerous and she was lucky to survive.

I came across the story of Elsie Hong Yet in Paul Yee's book *Saltwater City: an Illustrated History of the Chinese in Vancouver*. She had described to the author what a day in her life was like as a young worker, what work she did, and how she was treated by her mistress. In the book, she talks about hurting her leg badly, but she doesn't say how it happened. I imagined a scenario involving her chores. Elsie also said that her foot was saved from amputation because of her mistress's comment about how impossible it would be for her to find a husband without one. It sounded like a very tough job for anyone, but especially such a young girl. I bet you do some chores around your house, but I am pretty sure they aren't like Elsie's chores.

In the early 1900s, many young boys and girls came to Vancouver from China and then lived out their childhoods in service, just like Elsie. Laws against child labour were not enforced. Children were sold out of their families in China or Canada and placed in a household to work. The quality of their lives and the level of education they received depended entirely on the generosity of their masters and mistresses. Their freedom was limited and the expectations placed on their work were high. Almost every well-to-do household at the turn of the century in Vancouver had a Chinese servant.

By 1902, when Elsie was working for Yip Yee's second wife, Chinatown was a well-established neighbourhood in Vancouver. In fact, Chinese workers were some of the very first people to come to the area. The first Chinese to arrive in British Columbia came in 1778, to Nootka Sound as shipbuilders, but a much larger group arrived after 1858 via California, as a part of the Cariboo Gold Rush. Between 1881 and 1885, seventeen thousand Chinese came to Canada to work on the construction of the Canadian Pacific Railway. They earned exactly half the amount of money per day that other workers were paid due to the severe racial discrimination of that time. When the railway was completed in 1887—maybe you remember Minnie McCord seeing the first train come into Vancouver?—all Chinese workers found themselves out of a job. Many had a hard time finding new work because of racism. Non-Chinese workers started to complain that the Chinese were taking their jobs. Resentment ran high. The Canadian government passed a law forcing Chinese people to pay a "head tax" of fifty dollars to enter Canada, which was a lot of money in those days. The price of the head tax continued to go up, reaching five hundred dollars in 1903.

Tensions came to a head in 1907 when there were riots against the Chinese in Vancouver. The commotion went on for days. From 1923 to 1947, the Canadian government enforced the Chinese Exclusion Act, a racist policy that severely limited the number of Chinese people permitted to legally enter Canada.

Over time, tensions subsided. Today, Canada's Charter of Rights and Freedoms bans racial discrimination in all forms, and child labour is against the law.

People of Chinese ancestry now make up almost a third of Vancouver's population, and live in every corner of the city and its surrounding communities. The original Chinatown is recognized as a valuable historical neighbourhood in Vancouver and it is being restored. If you haven't visited there before, take a trip to Chinatown. A day spent there feels like a journey to a different time and place.

Robbery of the Century

George Lavery, age eleven
New Westminster, 1911

"You'll sit in that chair if you know what's good for you," I said, gesturing to a nearby log with my imaginary gun.

I practised my meanest and most terrifying facial expressions on the tree. I was pretending that the tree was Hong, the bank janitor. I had read about Hong in the newspaper and how the three masked men had surprised him on his way into the bank in the morning.

I had already read every article written about the robbery. Normally, reading the paper isn't a real perk of being a paperboy, but it sure has been for me since "the robbery of the century" a couple of days ago at the Bank of Montreal.

It's not just here in New Westminster that the robbery is making big news either. The story has appeared in newspapers around the world. No wonder, since they're saying it was the cleanest, best-planned, and biggest cash haul ever pulled off in the Western Hemisphere. The thieves got away with two hundred and fifty-eight thousand dollars and one hundred and fifty pounds of gold. I can't believe it happened right here in my town.

"You'd better not put up a fight," I said to the tree. "Or else . . ." I showed the tree my imaginary gun again. I pretended to tie Hong to a chair and gag him, just like the papers say the masked men did.

The idea that something so exciting happened here is taking up all the room in my head. This morning I couldn't possibly imagine sitting in my classroom and concentrating, so instead of walking into school, I walked right past it towards the ravine. Forget books today. I have a vault to blow up!

The newspaper said that the robbers dug underground to reach the bank safe. I grabbed a stick and stabbed it into the ground to dig my own hole. I looked back to make sure that my imaginary Hong was still tied up. "Better not move a muscle," I shouted at the tree. I dug as fast as I could because I needed to expose the vault quickly.

I picked up a bundle of sticks I'd tied with string. I handled it carefully because this was the nitroglycerin I needed to blow up the safe. One wrong move and I'd be blasted to bits. I tucked the sticks into the hole and ran for cover. I plugged my ears so I wouldn't hear the bang. The police still didn't know how the thieves managed the explosion so well. The people sleeping next door to the bank didn't even wake up.

I ran back to the hole and gathered all the imaginary money and gold. The papers said the getaway was quick because police found thousands of dollars of paper money spread across the floor of the bank. The robbers stuffed what they could into suitcases and ran.

"You'd better stay put, Hong!" I shouted. Then I remembered that the robbers wouldn't have known his name. Darn it. ". . . or whatever your name is . . ." I picked up my pretend suitcase and sprinted away from the scene of my pretend crime as fast as I could.

■ ■ ■

I whooped with joy. "The perfect getaway," I yelled to the trees. "The perfect crime!"

I kept running, thinking about how I would spend hundreds of thousands of dollars if I were a thief. I wondered how far away the real robbers were by now. They were probably in California. Riding in brand new cars and eating candy. I wished I were in their gang. I could be their leader. "George," they'd ask. "What's our next move?"

I slowed down to a walk, feeling out of breath. Then I sat down on the side of the ravine footbridge and opened my lunch sack. All that crime had made me hungry. I bit into my apple and thought about the food that really rich people eat. I had heard the fancy hotels in Vancouver served Russian caviar. How much caviar could I buy with one hundred and fifty pounds of gold, I wondered. Wait, wasn't caviar made of fish eggs? Yuck. Maybe I'd stick with apples.

As I chewed, something strange caught my eye underneath the footbridge. It looked like a bag tucked beneath the boards. Maybe someone had dropped it by mistake. I bent down and pulled it out into the open.

It was a little cloth pouch, all tightly bundled. I opened it up and peeked inside.

I blinked. It was stuffed full of money.

■ ■ ■

With the bag in my hand, I ran into the trees. Once I was quite far off the path, I stopped. I crouched and dumped the contents of the pouch onto the ground. Bundles of rolled-up money lay among the pine needles at my feet.

I sat down and started counting. I felt sweaty and hot. My heart was beating so quickly that I wondered for a moment if

I could be suffering a heart attack. I had no idea how long I was counting. It felt like hours. Finally, I finished. I had five thousand dollars in cash in piles between my legs.

I wondered if my imagination had finally gotten the better of me. Was this a coincidence, or could this money have come from the robbery?

Had I stumbled on the robbers' secret hiding place? Suddenly I was scared. I thought about the guns the thieves had used. Maybe their stash was booby-trapped. I started to pile the cash back into the bag.

There were only a few bills left on the ground when I stopped. What if I kept a little bit of the money for myself? The robbers might not even notice. And if they did, they'd have no idea who took it. What could they do? Go to the police? I laughed for a moment, imagining the thieves making a report that some of their loot had been stolen.

Before I could talk myself out of it, I stuffed the last of the money into my pocket, five hundred dollars worth. I ran as fast as possible back to the footbridge. I shoved the bag underneath the boards, pushing it back as far as I could until it was out of sight.

As I stood up, I had an odd feeling I was being watched. A shiver ran down my spine. I was being silly. Mother always told me that I had an overactive imagination. I just needed to leave and I'd feel better.

With the hairs on the back of my neck all standing on end, I ran across the bridge, farther into the ravine. The apple wasn't sitting well in my stomach. My insides were knotted. I could feel the lump that the money made in my pocket and I began to worry that I had made a mistake. How would I explain that amount of money to my parents? I wouldn't be able to spend it because as soon as I pulled it out, everyone would ask questions. I wished I'd left the money alone.

A figure appeared up ahead. He stepped out of the bush and stood in the middle of the path, blocking my way. I felt light-headed.

I barged ahead. "Excuse me, sir," I said, trying to run past as quickly as possible.

Without a word, the man grabbed my arm and spun me around to face him. I thought I might drop dead on the spot. I wriggled desperately, trying to break out of this grip. I looked at him and smothered a scream. One of his eyes was missing and his face was terribly scarred. The hold he had on my arm was like an iron vice, but oddly, he was only using one arm to hold me. I looked down and saw that his other arm was a stump.

"You have something that is mine," he growled in accented English.

My tongue felt like it filled my entire mouth. I couldn't speak a word.

"The money," he said. "In your pocket."

I rushed to get the bills out of my pants. I pulled my hand out of my pocket, dropping money all over the path. The man tossed me onto the ground and bent down to pick up the money. While he was kneeling, I scrambled to my feet.

I ran. I didn't dare look behind me. Did he have a gun? Was he going to chase me? I half expected to hear a shot ring out.

"Forget what you saw," he shouted after me.

In that moment, I would have promised him anything, but that was the one request that I knew was impossible. I would never, ever forget what I'd seen.

What do we know for sure?

It was a good thing that George Lavery didn't forget what he saw in the ravine. He eventually had to testify in the trial of John Bozyk, the man who grabbed him. His testimony was an important part of the case against the man. The boy must have been very scared to face Bozyk once again in the courtroom, but he did it.

When the New Westminster Bank of Montreal was robbed on September 15, 1911 the story became front-page news around the world because of the amount of money taken and the spectacular way it was stolen. The thieves made off with more than a quarter of a million dollars, which was an astronomical figure at the time. In today's money, it would be the same as more than five million dollars.

Incredibly, the robbers broke into the bank and blew up the vault without alerting the police, whose station was only twenty-one metres away. The police didn't know the robbery had taken place until ninety minutes later when Hong, the janitor, managed to untie his own hands and run out to sound the alarm. By that time, the thieves were gone.

At first, there were no leads. The police found an abandoned car that had been stolen for the getaway but the robbers hadn't been able to jumpstart it because it was missing a spark plug. They left the vehicle at the bottom of Royal Avenue's steep hill and found another way to escape.

Then city workers repairing the street at Fourth and Carnarvon found a huge stash of money. Just like the cash that George stumbled on in the ravine, it was stuffed under an old boardwalk. Unlike George, the city workers didn't try to keep any money. They called the police, who came and carried away twenty-three thousand and eighty dollars in evidence. They still didn't know who had committed the robbery, but they had some ideas.

John Bozyk, the man George met in the ravine, was arrested in Vancouver in October 1911. He was the prime suspect in the crime because of his history with the New Westminster police. He had lost his eye and his arm in an earlier dynamite explosion that police suspected he'd caused. Since the bank robbery had been conducted with explosives, he was at the top of the suspect list. Also, no one other than George Lavery had seen him since the night of the robbery.

After taking the money from George's pocket, Bozyk returned to the footbridge where the money was hidden. He took the five thousand dollars and fled to a Vancouver hotel, where he spent about three hundred dollars on a handgun and furniture. Even with George Lavery's testimony about the day in the ravine, the court found Bozyk guilty of possession of stolen money but not the original robbery.

In fact, no one was ever found guilty of the robbery itself. Eventually, six people including Bozyk were charged in connection with the crime. John McNamara was found guilty of attempting to steal the car that was left abandoned. Walter Davis pled guilty to possession of stolen money and served six months in jail. The other three men charged were acquitted. Most of the stolen money was never found.

I wish I knew what happened to George Lavery when he grew up. If you know, could you get in touch with me? I found this story in *New Westminster Album: Glimpses of a City as it Was*. I was reading about the bank robbery and thinking how exciting it was, wishing I could find a way to get it into this book. The last few sentences on the robbery in the book described the role young George Lavery played in the story. I felt like I had hit the jackpot. I can't be sure how George stumbled on the money. I know he was skipping school, and since everyone in town was talking about the robbery, I imagined that he might be re-enacting the robbery by himself in the woods. I like to think that George Lavery was just as intrigued by the story as I was. He just didn't know he'd be a part of it!

Balwant Singh with his father on board the *Komagata Maru*.

My Friend the Rat

Balwant Singh, age seven
Aboard the Komagata Maru, *Vancouver Harbour, 1914*

May 23, 1914

I've been two months on this ship, my little rat friend. It is too long.

You are a rat, you probably don't mind. A ship or a sewer, it is all the same to you. Not to me, though.

Two months of seeing only ocean. As far as I could see in every direction, only waves and sky. Water and air. It is a long, long way to Vancouver from my home.

Two months of swaying through the waves. I saw many men get sick. They throw up and up and up and up. At first I couldn't eat because when I think of all the throwing up, I want to throw up too. After so long on the sea, I don't care anymore. I eat anyway.

Two months with no friends, just you. I hope you don't mind that I keep you in this little cage. You keep me company. You are my only friend. There are many people on board, but only four children. One is just a baby girl, so she doesn't even count.

Some of the grown-up passengers are fun to play with, but they soon get bored with my games. The other kid is the boy from the family of the ship's doctor. The doctor tries to keep him separate from the rest of us. He thinks he's better than everyone. He thinks his son is too. Sometimes he lets his boy play with me, but only because I am the son of the man who organized this trip. I would rather play with you, little rat.

At least I am with my father, Baba Gurdit Singh.

Did I already tell you that my mother died when I was four months old? You don't have to be sad for me, little rat. I don't remember her. I have my father and that is all.

He organized this boatful of people to come to Canada. He sold the fares to everyone, promising that once we landed in Canada, we would be allowed to stay. He told these men that they could have a new life in a new country, a better life. So far, it is a life with a lot of throwing up. Do rats ever throw up? No, probably not.

But not for much longer. Today, we will arrive in Vancouver. Today we can get off the boat. Today is the start of a better life.

Oh, wait. Will you come with me? Do you want to be Canadian? I would like you to stay with me, friend.

I hear my father calling me. He says I should pull on my best clothes. Soon it will be time to go ashore. Get on your best fur suit, little rat. I am only teasing. I know you can't change. You look good just the way you are.

At least I have this little cabin to change in, Ratty. Father made sure I would have a private bed with him. The other fellows are packed into rows of hard benches for sleeping. I am happy to have my bed and a place to hide you and your cage. Don't I look fancy in these clothes? Father has kept them separate and clean in our trunk for the whole journey. He wants me to look tidy.

Let's go up on deck, little rat. Let's have a look. Maybe we can see Vancouver already. My legs are so excited to get off the ship and stand on the earth again. I want to be on solid ground. It can't be long now.

May 24, 1914

Oh, Ratty. When we didn't get off the ship yesterday, all the passengers were angry.

Today, everyone is grumpy. Are you grumpy? No, and that's why I love to talk to you, friend. You are happy wherever you are. I need to learn how to be like you.

My clean clothes are folded up inside the trunk again. Father told me to put them back. It is harder to be stuck on the ship when I thought we were so close to getting off. My legs feel itchy, like I have to move them all the time.

After two months of waiting, another day or two doesn't matter, right?

I can't help it. I feel very much like the men out on the deck. Their faces are stormy and impatient. My father seems flustered today too. When I asked him when we'll get off the ship, he didn't answer me. Even though I was standing right next to him in this tiny space, Ratty, it was like he was alone and someplace else.

My father sighed. His back was to me, so I couldn't see his face.

"It is just a matter of time, Father," I said to him. I hope I said the right thing.

June 26, 1914

Ratty, don't worry. Even though food supplies are is getting low on board the ship, I won't let you starve. I will always share my food with you.

I don't know why the people in Vancouver won't let us come to shore. Don't they know how little rations we have left? They must know. Father told me that the Canadians won't let supply ships come out to us. Some people in the Indian community in

Vancouver ignored them and came anyway. They sneaked out in boats to deliver food and drinks. I didn't see them, but I am grateful for their charity.

Four weeks sitting here in the harbour feels like torture to me. I know how you feel now, trapped in your cage. This boat is my cage.

I can see the land. I wonder if I could swim to shore. I could try. You could sit up on top of my head and stay dry. We could escape together. No. It's a bad idea. I don't think I can swim. It doesn't look that hard, but who knows? Can you swim, Ratty?

Do you want me to take you up to the deck, Ratty? Do you want to see Vancouver? From the deck, the city doesn't look that exciting. It doesn't look like the land of opportunity to me. It is much quieter than Hong Kong. I can see people, though. They stand on the dock to look at us. They just stare at our ship. I stare back.

I wonder what Vancouver looks like beyond the buildings on the water. Where do the people who are staring at me from the shore go home to? What are the children like? I wonder if they want me to come to their city, or if they want me to float away.

I hope that they are thinking welcoming thoughts.

I hear conversations. Not everyone on the *Komagata Maru* agrees about what to do, little rat. Some want to stay, some want to go. I just want to get off this boat.

July 2, 1914
It is so nice and cool in here. Oh Ratty, it is hot out on the deck of the ship. It feels good to get out of the sun. I'm sorry I'm so late with your food today. There is a lot of action out there and

I was trying to hear what people were saying. Father gets so impatient and angry when I ask too many questions. It is better to be quiet and listen to what others say.

Everyone was feeling a little bit hopeful before today. I don't know exactly what happened, but there was a lot of talk about a court case. The lawyer man from Vancouver came out to the ship today with news. I don't think it was good news. I could hear grumbles spreading through the crowd as the information from the lawyer spread from passenger to passenger. No one takes time to explain anything to me. I do my best to put it together but the pieces don't make sense.

I saw my father by himself earlier. He looked sad and disappointed. He was standing at the railing of the ship, looking out at Vancouver. I reached out for his hand. He took my hand and squeezed it very hard. I didn't think it was a good time to ask him anything. I just held his hand.

The only thing I understand is that there will be more waiting. I don't think we are waiting to get off anymore. I heard someone shouting that we couldn't leave without fresh supplies for the trip. Leave for where, I wonder?

I don't know if I will ever get off the *Komagata Maru*. Maybe I will become an old man on this ship. No matter how long we are on the boat, I will take care of you, Ratty. I will put extra food aside for you underneath my bed. I'll make sure you have enough.

July 19, 1914

I am scared. I feel better here with you, little rat. Cuddle up here, next to my cheek. You are so soft.

Out on the deck it is scary, Ratty. A tugboat is trying to tie up on the starboard side of the *Komagata Maru*. Onboard are many Vancouver police officers and other men. They have guns and they are shouting.

"They cannot make us leave like this," I heard a man scream when I was up there. "Do not let them tie up. Do not let them get on board."

The tugboat kept coming alongside our ship. The police were throwing ropes and trying to tie up to us. The men on board our ship all went to the railing. They threw whatever they could find down onto the men trying to come aboard. They threw bricks and coal down onto the police. The police fired warning shots into the air.

I went and hid behind a stack of boxes on the deck. I couldn't see my father. The noise and the shots frightened me. The air was warm, but I felt cold as I huddled behind the crates. I ran here, to you.

I wish my father were here. I hear loud noises everywhere. The sound of an axe chopping. More shots. Come closer, my little friend. We will protect each other.

July 23, 1914

Are you sleeping, Ratty? I know it's early, but it's time to wake up. I have a present for you. I want to let you go. I don't want you to be trapped anymore. Come here to say goodbye.

Can you hear the anchor chain lifting? We are leaving.

A huge navy ship is nearby, off our bow. It has big guns pointed at us. We have to sail away quickly. Maybe you can swim to Vancouver? Our ship is starting to move, but you still have time. Out you go, Ratty. You are free to go wherever you like.

What do we know for sure?

The *Komagata Maru* incident is part of a shameful time in Canada's history when our country's immigration policies did not treat all cultures equally.

The ship arrived in the Vancouver harbour with three hundred and seventy-six people aboard. The passengers included three hundred and forty Sikhs, twenty-four Muslims, and twelve Hindus—all from India. All of them were British subjects, just as Canadians were at the time. They were trying to immigrate to Canada. In a two-month journey, sailing from Singapore to Hong Kong to Shanghai, China, and then Yokahama, Japan, they crossed the Pacific to Vancouver but were not allowed to come ashore. There was a standoff. The Vancouver officials told the ship to leave and the passengers of the ship refused to go. To force the ship to depart, Vancouver officials refused them supplies. The government figured that with no food on board, the ship would eventually have to leave. The passengers on the ship refused to budge.

The facts and dates in this story are all true, including the fact that the young boy, Balwant Singh, was on board with his father. I learned about the *Komagata Maru* in school, but I didn't know there were kids on board the ship. Someone showed me a photograph of the boat's passengers and standing right at the front was a little boy. It was Balwant Singh. I did some research and read *The Voyage of the Komagata Maru: The Sikh challenge to Canada's Colour Bar* by Hugh J.M. Johnson. There was very little mention of Balwant and what life on board was like for him, so I used my imagination. There are always rats on ships, so I made up a rat friend for Balwant so that the boy could talk to him about his feelings. There was a lot of tension on the boat and I don't imagine the men were taking time to explain the situation to a seven-year-old. An animal would have been a good companion for a little guy in a very uncertain situation.

In the story, Balwant describes looking across the water at the people gathered on the shore to see the ship. That was true. The ship in the harbour was big news in Vancouver. The Indo-Canadian community in Vancouver organized a "shore committee." They raised money and staged protests to support the newcomers onboard the ship. On the other side, some other Vancouverites protested against allowing the passengers to come into the country.

There was a court case. The Sikh community in Vancouver raised funds to hire a lawyer to take the case to a hearing. Even though the passengers on the *Komagata Maru* believed they had a legal right to immigrate, the judge decided against them. He denied them entry because they had not come directly from India, but via Hong Kong.

In the story, Balwant witnessed a tugboat trying to tie up to the ship, and a violent encounter. More than one hundred and twenty-five police officers and thirty-five immigration officials on the *Sea Lion* tried to board the ship to force it to leave. Passengers fought them off. Eyewitnesses said that the tug was covered in coal when it retreated.

After two months anchored in Vancouver's harbour, the *Komagata Maru* was escorted the out of Canadian waters by the Canadian navy ship, the HMCS *Rainbow*.

The story doesn't end there, unfortunately. The ship didn't reach India until the end of September. The passengers had been onboard for more than five months, but they were not allowed to get off the boat in India because, after the standoff in Vancouver, the British colonial government there saw them as troublemakers. When police tried to arrest Baba Gurdit Singh, a fight broke out. The police fired their guns at the ship and twenty passengers were killed. Most of the passengers who survived were put in jail.

Balwant's father escaped, but he turned himself into authorities in 1922 and served five years in prison. Balwant grew up and had a family of his own in India.

It was not until 2008 that Prime Minister Stephen Harper offered an apology for the way the *Komagata Maru* incident had been handled. The BC government passed a motion making an official apology, saying, "the House deeply regrets that the passengers, who sought refuge in our country and our province, were turned away without benefit of the fair and impartial treatment befitting a society where people of all cultures are welcomed and accepted." In December 2010, the federal government also committed funds for a memorial and a museum dedicated to the incident.

In the summer of 2010, a boatful of refugees from Sri Lanka came into Victoria, BC, and a debate began again over the people who should stay, and the people who should go. Canada is still seen by many people as a place of safety and opportunity for people from other countries.

How did your family get to Canada? Are you a First Nations kid with family origins in that go back for many centuries in North America, or does your family have a recent immigration story? Maybe you'd like to find out.

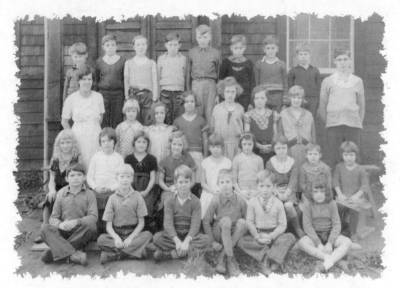

Roche Point School, Class of 1933. Bertha Patterson is the tallest girl in the third row and her brother, Lloyd, is on the far left in the back row.

Don't Be Such a Chicken

Bertha Patterson, age ten
North Vancouver, 1932

"Bertha, run and get Mrs. Cooper a glass of lemonade," my mama told me. I did as she asked right away. I knew how hard social calls were for her right now. For all of us, really.

"Yes, Mama," I said. I walked to the kitchen area and got a clean glass.

"I wish I could offer you something more civilized than this, Jane," my mama went on. "We're still waiting." This last sentence she almost shouted, tossing her words over her shoulder in the hope that someone inside the house would hear her. They might hear her, but they probably wouldn't care.

She was yelling at our so-called neighbours, but I wasn't sure that word was right for this situation. Our neighbours were actually living in our house. Want to know where we live? On the front porch. I'm not complaining. I know we are lucky to be together and the porch is huge. Good thing too, since there are seven of us kids, plus my mama.

It's a funny story how we ended up on the porch. Well, not really. When we left our house last year, we told some people that they could stay in it. Times were hard, not just for us, but for everyone. My parents thought that it was the right thing to do. Do you know what wasn't nice, though? When we came back a couple of months ago, without my dad since he'd died while we were gone, those people wouldn't leave. I guess they liked it here.

My mama isn't the type to take something like that sitting down. Well actually, I guess she did sit down, right on the porch, and she told those people that she wasn't budging until they moved along.

"Well," said Mrs. Cooper, "I don't know how they live with themselves when they see you with the children, a baby even, living on this porch. In your own house, no less."

Yep, a baby too. Baby Bessie came along two months after we lost my dad. That sounds like bad luck, but she's such a good girl that I sure think we're lucky.

I brought Mrs. Cooper her lemonade.

"Thank you, child," she said. She always calls each of us "child." That might be because she doesn't know which of us is which.

"They tell me that they're making plans to go somewhere else," my mama said. "But they've been saying the same thing for two months."

"I don't know how you manage," said Mrs. Cooper.

"Oh, we're fine, aren't we, Bertha?" said Mama, turning to me.

"You bet," I said.

"All I need to do is figure out some way to earn more money," said Mama. "Since Norman died, that part is hard. Along with a lot of things, I suppose." Mama sighed, but she smiled at the same time. "We make do. It isn't an easy time for anyone."

"Speaking of that," said Mrs. Cooper, "My next-door neighbour, old Mr. Stewart, took sick and left to go back to the Prairies where his daughter lives. It might be a one-way trip, if you know what I mean. Well, since then, these awful raccoons have been terrorizing the chickens he left behind. Oh, there must have been about twenty-four to start, but they're getting picked off one by one, every night. I was thinking, you'd be doing those hens a favour if you rescued them from those raccoons."

My mama looked over to me, one eyebrow raised, a little smirk playing on her mouth.

"Well, we can't just walk over there and take them," she said. "Though the eggs would be welcome," she added, never taking her eyes off me.

"Think of it as a rescue, Bessie," said Mrs. Cooper. "You'd be saving their scrawny necks from the raccoons. The raccoons don't need those birds. Those beasts have plump bellies, not like you lot . . ." Mrs. Cooper stopped. I knew why. She didn't want to offend my mama.

Well fine, we weren't exactly fat, but we weren't wasting away either. Our mama knew how to make delicious food out of almost nothing, like magic nearly. We did just fine, thank you very much. But heavens me, those eggs would be delicious. I could already smell them frying in butter in my mama's old cast iron pan.

"You know, Bertha," said Mrs. Cooper, looking over at me. "Maybe you should bring your mama over for a visit with me tomorrow. You could go for a little walk while we chat. Wouldn't that be nice?"

A walk? More like a chicken hunt. I knew exactly what she was saying and I couldn't wait to rescue those chickens.

■ ■ ■

My brother Lloyd, my mama, and I walked along the side of the road to Mrs. Cooper's the very next day. Mama was going to tea and Lloyd and I were on a mission. I called it Operation Scrambled

Egg. I was carrying three burlap sacks, one for each of us.

"I'll be at Mrs. Cooper's for twenty minutes or so," Mama told us. "Meet me on the edge of her yard and we'll walk back together."

"Got it," said Lloyd. I was excited about the fresh eggs we'd get from the chickens, but Lloyd was far more thrilled by the mission itself. I'd asked him to come with me because I knew he'd be the perfect partner in crime.

When we got to Mrs. Cooper's yard, Mama went in the gate, while we walked along the fence in the other direction.

"Have a pleasant walk, children," Mama called out as she shut the gate behind her.

We darted into the woods, towards old Mr. Stewart's place. Lloyd was taking his job a little too seriously for my liking. He was hiding behind trees, racing from one trunk to another as if being chased.

"What are you doing, Lloyd?" Talk about looking suspicious!

"Just scanning for spies and informants," he said, popping up from behind a bush.

"Oh brother," I said. "We don't have that long, so let's keep moving." Lloyd's shoulders slumped and he came over to walk next to me. We walked along in silence for a couple of minutes, but as we got closer to the Stewart place, the sound of clucking filled the air.

"Bingo!" shouted Lloyd.

"Shhhh!" I warned him. "Why don't you just put a sign on the road announcing what we're doing? Shush down."

We walked across the yard towards the chicken coop. I peered inside. There were only nine hens left. Those raccoons had been feasting. It was a good thing we hadn't waited any longer, or they'd all be gone.

I pulled out the burlap sacks. "Three in each," I told my brother.

Well, that was easier said than done. I managed to grab two off their roosts, but the raccoon attacks had made these hens skittish. They bolted out all over the yard. Lloyd and I raced around after them.

"Bertha, you're running around like a chicken with its head cut off . . . get it? Like a chicken with its head cut off? Ha!"

"You are so corny," I said, but I had to laugh a little bit. I stuck my arms out from my sides like wings and clucked a little bit. Then Lloyd did the same thing. We were laughing so hard that we were having no success grabbing the chickens at all.

"Ha . . . ha, ha . . . get the . . . chickens, Lloyd," I sputtered. We couldn't stop giggling, but managed to capture all of the chickens eventually.

You know, it isn't an easy thing to carry two bags of angry, clucking, pecking chickens. They were going a little bit bananas inside those bags. I had to carry my bag and my mama's, while Lloyd was struggling with just one.

So much for being quiet. We marched back to the place where we were supposed to meet mama, but those chickens were so loud, it was impossible to sneak around.

"Maybe we should wring their necks and have chicken for dinner," said Lloyd. "It'd be quieter, at least."

"But all those yummy eggs," I said. "This is Operation Scrambled Egg, not Operation Roast Chicken."

Lloyd shrugged. We reached the gate where we'd left Mama

and found her there, waiting for us. "Success, I see," she said.

"Only nine, but pretty good," I told her loudly over the squawking.

"Well, we'll have to walk along the road to get home. If you hear a car coming, jump into the woods or the ditch. If anyone sees us with these big sacks full of chickens, there'll be some tough questions."

Who was going to give my mama trouble? I knew it was hard times and all, but a widow with seven kids living on the porch of the house her husband had built with his own two hands? She should be able to borrow a few chickens that no one was using.

We started out for home. Mama was jiggling the sack of chickens like it was a baby. Her hens quieted right down. I tried that; it didn't work. Maybe I wasn't jiggling right?

"I hear a car," Lloyd said. We stopped and listened. Sure enough, I could hear an engine in the distance too.

"C'mon kiddos, into the ditch," said Mama.

We all jumped off the side of the road and hunkered down in the ditch, ducking our heads below the level of the road. While we waited for the car to pass us by, Mama started to giggle.

"What's so funny?" I asked her.

"I'm not sure," she laughed. "Something about the three of us hiding in a ditch with bags of chickens. It just strikes me as ridiculous. Oh, your father would have found this hilarious. Shhhh."

Just then, the car sped past. It didn't even slow down, so I guess the driver couldn't see us. We stood up and brushed ourselves off to keep walking. Jumping around so much had riled up the chickens again.

"Bertha, you picked a perfect name: Operation Scrambled Egg. These birds are so fidgety. Their eggs will be scrambled nicely," said Mama. She was still giggling.

We had to jump into the ditch four more times on the way home. One time, Lloyd let go of the top of his sack and a chicken escaped. Luckily, we tracked her down. She was so frightened that she barely went anywhere.

The three-mile walk home went by quickly. We sang all the songs we knew with chickens in them, then all the ones with eggs in them. There weren't that many. Then we changed the words of the songs we knew so they would be about chickens. We made up some funny ones.

"*Once I built a railroad . . .*" I sang, "*Now it's done. Brother can you spare a chicken?*"

My brother laughed.

My favourite game on the way home was thinking of all the things we could make with the eggs: cakes, omelettes, Yorkshire puddings, Easter eggs, pancakes. The list went on and on. Mama said she'd try them all.

When we got home, we dumped out the chickens in our front yard. We had an old chicken coop already, so they just moved on in. Those hens made themselves right at home. I gave them a bit of feed and it was just like they'd always been there.

I looked at Mama, up on the porch holding the baby. She was laughing and telling the other kids about our adventure. I liked seeing her smile.

"When we heard a car coming up the road," said Lloyd, "we had to dive for cover." He demonstrated what we looked like jumping into the ditch. They were all laughing.

With a bunch of chickens about, plus our old goats, things were starting to look like old times around here, like back in the days before Dad died. Living on the porch of our old house was far from normal, but one look at the happiness on my mother's face and the smiles of my brothers and sisters told me that we were on the right track.

What do we know for sure?

As winter crept closer to North Vancouver in 1932, Bertha Patterson and her family finally moved back inside their home. It was good timing because the family wasn't looking forward to spending winter living outdoors on the front porch. It seems like a crazy situation to us today, but Bertha described a true situation; times were tough in those days.

Canada was enduring the Great Depression, which started in 1929 and ended in 1939. It was a worldwide crisis, but Canada and the United States were hit very badly. Men and women all over our country were out of work, so money was very tight for nearly every family. It was one of the most difficult periods in Canadian history.

People moved across the land to search for paying work, but many people found none. Since Vancouver has milder weather than most of Canada and it lies at the western end of the railway, many men ended up living around the city in temporary camps called "hobo jungles." Vancouver was said to be the only town in Canada where you could starve before freezing to death.

Few women could find jobs outside the home at that time, but that didn't stop many wives and mothers from inventing creative ways to earn a bit of extra money for their families. Some took in sewing, or cleaned other people's homes. Bessie Patterson, for instance, sold goat's milk to her neighbours. Her children picked wild berries when they were in season, and Bessie sold them.

The Patterson family lived in the Deep Cove area of North Vancouver, very close to where Captain George Vancouver's men had camped in the second story in this book. The Pattersons built the house themselves on six parcels of uncleared land they purchased. The property was completely covered in trees. Apparently, there were so many thick trees and so much undergrowth that they couldn't even get horses into the woods to help clear it. Before he died, Norman Patterson worked in a lumber mill, so he was able to obtain cheap lumber. With a lot of hard work and long hours, he managed to build a comfortable home for his family.

Can you imagine how frustrated Bessie Patterson must have felt when the family that had borrowed her home refused to move out? Bertha and her brothers and sisters lived on that front porch for months. Like Bertha said in the story, the hard times were bad enough that they still felt lucky to have a place of their own—even if it was just a porch.

Life was tough, but that doesn't mean that the Patterson kids sat around feeling miserable and sorry for themselves. Canadian kids still had a lot of fun during the Depression, even though grown-ups had lots of worries. The Patterson kids used to go on day trips into town for picnics in Stanley Park or at Boundary Bay. They enjoyed swimming when the weather was mild. They thought nothing of swimming across Indian Arm, from Deep

Cove over to Belcarra and back. They must have been great swimmers, because that's a long way. For them, even an outing to snag chickens could be fun.

Bertha and Lloyd Patterson told historians from the Deep Cove Historical Society about the day they rescued the chickens with their mother. The Society was doing research for their book, *Echoes Across the Inlet,* which they published in 1989. Both the book and the excellent local museum offer a comprehensive overview of their history of Deep Cove. In their interview, the Pattersons recalled that their mother's kind friend was very careful not to suggest that they steal chickens. She made sure to describe the idea as a "rescue" because she didn't want to injure Mrs. Patterson's pride, even though she knew what those eggs would mean to the family.

The Pattersons weathered the storm of the Depression and today the family still owns the same parcel of land in North Vancouver where this story took place.

Duncan, the tallest boy, with his brothers and sister.

Broken Promises

Duncan May, age eleven
Sea Island, Richmond, 1934

"Look, there's Rusty," shouted my brother John. "Come here, boy."

Rusty was our collie. Our father used him in the fields with the cows, but when Rusty wasn't working, he loved to play with us. He bounded up the field.

We were walking home after wading in the Fraser River all afternoon. It was one of the first hot days of spring, and since it was a Saturday, my two brothers, my sister, and I had stolen a few hours away from our farm chores to have some fun. Once the weather shifted from cool and wet to warm and less wet, one of our favourite things to do was to find a hollow in the riverbank carved out by tides. The shallow water warmed up in the sun and made for an ideal swimming hole.

Rusty caught up to us and ran circles around our legs, wagging his tail happily. We stopped walking to pet him.

"Duncan, quit it," Rosemary said to me as I stroked the dog. "Keep walking. Mother needs me home."

Poor Rosemary. At seven, she was the youngest of us and the only girl, so her voice was often drowned out by us boys. For the last half hour at the river she'd been pestering us to leave. Now that we had finally headed home, we were dawdling. Mother expected her to get home in time to help with supper.

"Norm, John, c'mon, let's keep moving," I said. I was the oldest, but not by much. Barely a year separated each of us three boys, so my brothers didn't pay me much mind. Occasionally they listened. We set out again and Rosemary shot me a grateful look.

"Let's play tag," I said. "But the rule is, you have to be running towards the house." That should help us get home faster, I thought. "You're it, Norm." I tagged him on the shoulder.

The four of us ran. Norm quickly tagged Rosemary, who set off as fast as her legs would carry her. She was still no match for a ten-year-old. I slowed up a touch and circled back. She spotted me and slapped my shoulder after a burst of speed.

The game of tag had worked. We got home quickly and once the house was in sight, Rosemary sprinted ahead to join our mother in the kitchen. She was still just a wee bit of a girl, but getting to be a good cook. It wasn't that surprising, since she learned from our mother, the best cook on Sea Island.

Just then, one of the barn cats caught Rusty's eye. He bolted after it, nearly taking out Norm's legs along the way. Norm jumped aside at the last second, avoiding a fall.

"Good thing my reflexes are as good as the cat's," he said.

"Not too sure about that," joked John.

Suddenly, we heard frantic barking from the barn.

"Sounds like Rusty might have that cat cornered," I said.

"Cornered the cat, huh? Pretty slow cat. I guess you do have a cat's reflexes after all, Norm," said John.

"I think there are kittens in there," I said. "Let's go make sure they're alright."

The three of us entered the barn and sure enough, the cat was guarding the litter of kittens she had hidden in a pile of hay in the corner. She was hissing and Rusty was in front of her barking his head off.

"C'mon, Rusty. C'mon, boy. This way," John managed to get between cat and dog, shooing Rusty away and out the big barn doors. To keep him away from the kittens, which were mewing madly, Norm shut the doors behind him.

We went over to make sure the kittens were unharmed.

"You might have the reflexes of one of these cats, Norm," I said, pointing down at the pile of fumbling, blind kittens. We had to laugh, even Norm.

"Let's see you catch me then," said Norm as he sprang up and ran to the opposite side of the barn.

I started after him. We bobbed between the hoes, rakes, and bags of feed and seed stacked high, up and down, in and out of the loft. Norm just managed to avoid my reach at every turn. Finally, I trapped Norm behind the thresher. It was a standoff. We stood there, out of breath, eyeing each other. Norm faked going to his left and I went for it, leaving Norm an easy out to his right.

He ran as fast as he could around the back of the thresher. As he came around the corner, his right foot slipped on a clump of hay and slid right out from under him. He went down hard, crashing into the wall of the barn with a sickening thud.

Silence. For a moment we heard nothing except for the mewing of the kittens. John and I ran to Norm's side. He didn't look good. His skin was a dull grey colour and his eyes were closed, but he was moaning a little bit. A tear seeped out from under his eyelashes and ran down his cheek.

"Norm," I said. "Norm, where does it hurt?"

". . . Arm," he said.

We both leaned in to see. His arm looked a little funny, sort of crooked.

John and I exchanged looks. This was bad news. The last time we'd been caught playing in the barn, our father had threatened us with the strap. He had never hit us boys, but the threat of it was bad enough. That time we'd come to no harm, but he told us never to play in the barn again on account of how dangerous it was with all the farm equipment.

"Norm, maybe if you get up, you'll feel better," I said.

"It might not be so bad," John whispered.

Norm just moaned some more.

John and I each took one of Norm's armpits and pulled him to his feet. His face went from grey to pasty white.

"Norm, you're going to be fine," I said. "A bit of supper in you and you'll feel brand new."

". . . I don't think so," he muttered. "It hurts bad."

"We'll all be in rough shape if Father finds out that we were fooling around in the barn, Norm. You can't let on."

"Please, Norm," said John.

Our wincing brother nodded his head, his face as white as a tablecloth.

Rosemary pulled open the barn doors.

"What are you doing in here with the doors closed?" she asked. "Supper's almost on the table. Come in and wash up."

■ ■ ■

Norm hadn't said a word since we'd come in the house. He was holding his arm like a bird with a broken wing. To make up for his silence, John and I talked a blue streak while Norm pushed peas around on his plate.

"Norm, we don't leave food on our plates," said our mother. "Eat up."

She started telling us again that lots of people in Canada

didn't have enough to eat. "We're lucky we live on a farm," she said. "We can grow a lot of our own food." Our mother preserves everything she can, from the wild berries we pick in the summer to the extra eggs the hens lay for us. Nothing is allowed to go to waste.

Sometimes, strangers knock on the door looking for a meal. Men without work wander from farm to farm, searching for a day's wages or food in exchange for their hard work in the fields. Mother never turns away a hungry man, even if there is no work for them. "If someone is in need, we share," she says.

One evening not so long ago, a stranger arrived. He had travelled across the province looking for work with no success. We didn't have a job for him, but Mother set him a place at our supper table. When she brought his plate to the table, she apologized that the meat was tough. This gentleman looked up at her and said, "it's a darn sight tougher when there is none, ma'am."

Mother reminded us how fortunate we were to go to bed with full stomachs each night, for there were lots of kids who didn't.

Tonight, Norm didn't take a single bite. When Mother called him out, he did his best, but no matter how much he chewed a mouthful, he couldn't seem to swallow it.

"Mother," he said. "I don't feel well. May I be excused?"

"You don't look very good," she said. "Come let me feel your forehead."

While Norm walked around the table to our mother, John and I held our breath. "You feel clammy," she said. "Leave your plate on the counter and go up to bed. I'll check on you." She planted a kiss on his check.

"Do you boys feel alright?" our father asked from the other end of the table.

We both nodded mutely.

I was getting worried. Maybe Norm was badly hurt. John, Rosemary and I did our evening chores. I kept one ear open for the creak of the steps. What if Norm came downstairs and confessed everything?

I thought about how my father used to joke about selling us kids to his customers when we went out delivering hay. On Sundays, we rode into Vancouver with a wagon piled sky-high with fresh cut hay. When we were little, he used to offer us for sale, fifteen cents apiece. One time, a customer paid up. I actually saw him hand over the money. I was terrified that I had been sold. As I got ready for bed that night, I wondered what would happen if father found out the truth about Norm's injury. Maybe he wouldn't sell us. Maybe he'd just give us away.

John, Norm, and I shared a room. Usually, our favourite nighttime game was jumping from bed to bed until Mother or Father came upstairs. Not tonight. John and I walked into our room and quietly climbed into our beds. Norm looked like he was already asleep, but even sleeping he looked like a kid in pain.

John and I said quiet goodnights and extinguished our lantern, both of us hoping that Norm would wake up all better.

■ ■ ■

"Ah!" I lifted my head from my pillow and listened hard. What in heaven was that? It was the middle of the night, still pitch black outside, still too early to get up to milk the cows. I jumped up at the same time as Mother burst into the room.

It was Norm, screaming in agony.

Mother gathered him up in her arms and carried him out of the room and downstairs. John and I lay in bed, listening to our Mother and Father debate what to do. Norm was whimpering in the background. We couldn't hear what he was saying, but it seemed clear that the gig was up. We were in trouble. Poor Norm. Poor us.

A few minutes passed with more discussion downstairs, just slightly out of earshot. Then, the sound of our father's footsteps on the stairs. The door opened. The glow of a lantern came into the room and we looked up to see our father framed in the doorway.

"Boys, get dressed and come downstairs," he said.

Uh oh.

What do we know for sure?

Norm's arm was broken. He tried to be brave, but the pain was too much. He woke up the whole house at 2:00 AM and the truth came out.

Duncan, John, and Norm got in trouble for playing in the barn, but since they were mischievous and energetic young boys, it wasn't the first, nor the last time that they were disciplined for their misadventures. One of Duncan's mother's favourite punishments for the boys was putting each of them in a different section of the yard. One was sent to the calf pen, another to the chicken yard, and the last to the main yard. What she didn't know was that as soon as her back was turned, the boys congregated in the back corner where the three yards met up. They would happily continue their games there.

Duncan had extremely fond memories of growing up on the family farm. He was very close to his parents and siblings. They worked hard, played hard, and ate well. Each morning before school, Duncan got up while it was still dark outside to milk the cows by lantern light. By the time he came in from the barn, his mother would have breakfast on the table and his lunch packed for school. The four Mays headed off for a day of learning at Bridgeport Elementary School, then back home for more chores. Duncan hauled wood, chopped kindling, fed the animals, and cleaned out the dairy every day.

When they weren't working, they had fun. Duncan remembers hours spent playing sports with his father and siblings. It was lacrosse in the warm-weather months and ice hockey when it was freezing. The family took day trips into Vancouver, or took an old boat or ferry to Hopkin's Landing or Boundary Bay. Duncan told me that it was a great place to be a kid. ·

Sea Island still has farm land on it, but not nearly as much as it did when Duncan was growing up. Originally Duncan's mother's family, the McDonalds, owned two hundred acres of land on Sea Island. In fact, you have probably been on their land. Today, it is the Vancouver International Airport. Richmond's McDonald Beach is also on old McDonald family land.

If you compare Duncan's life to Bonnie Patterson's from the previous story, you get an idea of how lucky the Mays were to live on a farm during such a tough time for the economy. Life was far from luxurious for them during the Depression—they didn't get electricity in the farmhouse until 1935—but farmers were self-employed and able to harvest food from their own land. It wasn't an easy time, but the Mays were some of the lucky ones.

Duncan and his brothers all grew up to be farmers. At twenty years old, Duncan had to take over responsibility for the family farm with his younger brothers due to the tragic death of their father. The May family suffered from a very odd August 11 curse. Duncan's grandfather was killed by a bull on August 11, 1923. Exactly twenty years later, on August 11, 1943, his father was also killed by a bull on the family farm. Two years later, on August 11, 1945, Duncan was nearly killed in a serious car accident. While August 11 brought bad luck, Duncan enjoyed lots of good luck on Sea Island. He married and had five sons of his own, all of whom still farm in Richmond.

I met Duncan May five years ago when I interviewed him to capture his life story for his family. I loved listening to him talk about growing up in Richmond. I knew that I wanted to share his stories with you, but when I tried to get in touch with him, I was saddened to learn that Duncan passed away in the summer of 2010 at eighty-seven years old.

I am happy that his stories can live on in this book; I think he would be too.

Keith with his model plane club. He is in the
back row, fifth from the right, wearing a hat.
BEEDIE FAMILY COLLECTION

Keith Beedie.
BEEDIE FAMILY COLLECTION

V is for Victory—T is for Trouble

Keith Beedie, age thirteen
Kerrisdale, 1939–1940

September 10, 1939

"Mum, it smells like my egg is burning," I shouted as I dragged myself downstairs for breakfast.

It was a school day. There was nothing to look forward to but a burnt egg for breakfast, followed by hours spent at an uncomfortable desk. The school year had just started again and already I was dreading the long days. After a summer holiday of building model airplanes on my own schedule, the last thing I wanted to do was sit in a classroom.

I learned more making planes than I did in school anyway. I wanted to be a pilot, so I figured it was more important to understand a plane's wing construction than how to dissect a frog. Maybe I struggled to find Froggy's liver, but I could build a Curtiss Robin airplane to scale from memory. That was a real skill in my books.

I'd started building planes with my dad when I was six years old. Seven years on, my whole ceiling was crammed with dangling models. The airspace in my bedroom was getting crowded. The planes were feather light, constructed out of balsa wood and rice paper, so the slightest wind caused them to crash into one another. If I left my window open, I could lie on my bed and imagine a dogfight overhead as the planes swayed and soared in the breeze. I could almost hear the scream of the dive-bombing aircraft slicing through the sky of my bedroom.

It doesn't take much imagination these days to conjure up

a high-stakes fight. A week ago, Britain declared war on Nazi Germany. There haven't been any battles yet, but I hope they start soon. They have already begun in my head, as I spend hours picturing the fights in my imagination. But instead of staying home and dreaming of aerial battles in Europe, I have to go to school and learn to use a protractor, or something else equally useless.

As I rounded the corner towards the kitchen, I stopped in my tracks. There was a sound coming from inside the kitchen that I had never heard before. If I didn't know better, I'd think that noise was my mother crying. Mother didn't cry, so it had to be something else. My ears strained to make sense of the sounds, but the radio was on and the grease from my breakfast egg was spitting loudly on stove.

With my feet still frozen in place, I stuck my head into the room. Mother was sitting at the kitchen table with a dishtowel balled in her fist. She had tears on her cheeks. In the pan, my egg was rapidly blackening around the edges.

"... *this morning, these measures were supplemented by others, including the Proclamation of the Defence of Canada regulations* ..."

It was the voice of Prime Minister Mackenzie King on the radio. The words he spoke went off like fireworks in my brain. It was finally official. Canada was at war. I looked over at my mother. I had never seen her cry before. Where was her sense of adventure? Europe is a long way away. What did she have to be sad about? As I scraped my charred egg onto a plate, I smiled. My school day had just become a lot more exciting.

May 1940

"Mum, can I have this old kettle for the Victory Drive?" I asked as I rummaged through the cupboards. Ever since Canada joined the war, Vancouver has jumped into action. There are collections for everything from money to metal.

I was gathering up everything I could for the war effort. Every scrap of metal was useful, we were told. I figured it was true. Bullets were tiny and we needed lots.

The idea was that if we could devote all our resources early on in the war, it would be over quickly. Secretly, I didn't want the fighting to end too quickly. I held on to a tiny hope that if the war lasted long enough, I'd be old enough to join the Royal Canadian Air Force and learn to fly a fighter plane. Eighteen was a terribly long time off, though. Victory was more important. So if clearing out my mother's cupboards helped, I was all for it.

I could see my mother out of the corner of my eye. She was reading my thoughts. She knew that if I had my way, I'd bundle up every baking tin and pan in the house.

"I'm watching you, Keith,' she said. "The Allies need planes and bombs, but I need my pots too."

"The kettle?" I asked again.

"Fine," she said. "But that's it for now. We're doing our part."

That was exactly the problem, I thought. I didn't feel like I was doing my part at all. As the months went on I wanted to do more. I couldn't march off to the recruitment office like I'd seen the older boys in the neighbourhood do, but there had to be something worthwhile I could do.

■ ■ ■

"Mum, I need our juice pitcher," I shouted as I ran into the kitchen from outside.

"What?" she asked. "Why? You aren't collecting glass now too, are you? There'll be nothing left in here soon."

"No," I said. "Glass is useless for the war. You can have it back when I'm done. I need it to serve the lemonade at my lemonade booth for the Air Supremacy Drive."

My mother reluctantly pulled out the pitcher. "Don't break it," she said as she handed it over. I barely heard her. I was already out the door.

As soon as I heard about the Air Supremacy Drive raising money to build more planes, I knew I had found my war contribution. I had the perfect idea. I spent my whole weekend constructing the lemonade stand from scratch out of scrap materials I found in our basement and garage.

Our house was only a couple of blocks from the Quilchena golf course. Every weekend, I watched golfers cross Arbutus Street to get to the other side of the course. My plan was to set up the lemonade stand on the sidewalk right next to the crosswalk. I would offer cold drinks for free in exchange for a donation to the Air Supremacy Drive. Who could say no to that?

I ran outside with the pitcher from my mother and stood back to admire my handiwork.

The booth looked great. I had even constructed a tiny overhang on the roof to offer a bit of shade to my customers but there was still a little something missing. It was a bit too plain. It needed a bit of gussying up to attract the attention I wanted.

I ran back into the basement to see if I could find anything extra to add a touch of pizzazz to the stand. As I moved a couple of boxes around, a flash of silver fabric caught my eye. I pulled it out. It was perfect. It was shiny and bright. Silver like that would shimmer in the sunlight. No one could walk past a stand covered in this!

I spent the next couple of hours smoothing the fabric over the outside of the booth. I got out every wrinkle. It looked dynamite. I was ready for business.

Once I set up at the crosswalk, I couldn't keep up with the demand. I was so busy that some people put in money and left without a drink. It was a massive success.

"Good for you, son," said a passing golfer. He took a long sip of lemonade and slipped an extra dollar bill into my collection can. "We need all we can spare for the effort."

"Thank you, sir," I said.

"Hitler is on the move, so we have to stay a step ahead," he went on. "He's in Holland and Belgium now, but we'll stop him."

"Yes, sir!" I grinned.

At the end of the day, I came home with thirty-nine dollars to donate to the Air Supremacy Drive. I had never felt better.

■ ■ ■

"Keith, come to the dinner table," shouted my mom from inside the house.

I walked in from the backyard, washed my hands, and sat down next to my sister Joan at the table. Mother set down the bread in front of me.

"Did you see your dad out there, Keith?" she asked.

"Nope. I think he's in the basement," I said, reaching for a slice.

My mother walked to the basement door and opened it, yelling down to my father. "Reg, dinner is on table."

"I'll be there in a minute," he yelled up. "I'm packing for my trip and I can't find my things for the movie." My father worked for a car manufacturer and one of his responsibilities was making presentations about new models to dealerships around the province. We could hear him shuffling boxes around downstairs. "Have you seen my movie screen?" he shouted.

I froze. The bread I'd been chewing turned to sawdust in my mouth. The screen. I got a sickening feeling in the pit of my stomach. I knew exactly where it was: cut up into pieces and nailed to the outside of my lemonade stand.

I felt like throwing up. I got up and walked down to the basement. My dad was on his knees, peering behind the shelves lining the walls.

"Dad," I said. I took a deep breath. "I used your screen for my Air Supremacy Drive stand."

"What do you mean?" he asked, getting up. "You didn't take it outside, did you? You didn't get it dirty?" The words wouldn't come out. When I opened my mouth to tell my father what had happened to the screen, I could only make a funny choking sound. I took a deep, deep breath and tried again. I explained how I'd cut the screen up to decorate the stand. For a couple of moments, my Dad didn't say a word.

"That thing was expensive," Dad finally said.

"I raised almost forty dollars," I said, barely above a whisper.

■ ■ ■

I paid my Dad back, every penny, but it hurt me to think that all the money I earned to pay my debt to him was going into a movie screen and not to new airplanes.

Even though it was a painful lesson, I was happy with my first contribution. I lay on my bed and stared up at my model planes doing battle on my ceiling and I felt good. I'd done something worthwhile. Somewhere in Europe, my thirty-nine dollars was part of a plane that wasn't made of balsa wood and rice paper. It was made of real steel and glass and it was fighting the German Luftwaffe.

Switching on the news on the radio, I heard the announcer say that the war was taking longer to win than they'd thought. Maybe I'd get a chance to fly that plane I'd helped build after all.

What do we know for sure?

Keith Beedie continued to contribute to the war effort as he grew older, and the Second World War dragged on.

Boeing, the airplane manufacturer, set up three factories to build planes in the Vancouver area during the war. There was one factory in Coal Harbour, one close to Terminal Avenue, and one at the airport in Richmond. Keith spent the summer between Grade Nine and Grade Ten as an assistant at the Richmond factory, then left school after completing Grade Ten to work in the factory full-time. One of his favourite jobs was riveting the bolts into the wings of the *Catalina* airplanes.

The three Boeing factories closed down shortly after the war ended in 1945, but the housing development built to house the workers for Boeing still exists close to the airport in Richmond. It is called Burkeville, named after Stanley Burke, who was then president of Boeing. The neighbourhood has three hundred and twenty-eight houses on roads named for different airplanes. Boeing later offered the houses for sale to returning veterans of the war. Many of these homes are still standing.

Keith almost got his wish to serve overseas in the war. He joined the RCAF in April 1944 but had to wait until his eighteenth birthday in June to start training. Keith turned eighteen the same week that the Allied troops landed on the beaches of Normandy in France. Keith did not get overseas, but he did serve his country for nine months.

The war lasted from 1939 to 1945, much longer than anyone had expected. Canada fought on the Allied side, with the United States, the United Kingdom, and other nations. Our country played a critical role in the Allied victory, particularly after D-Day when the Canadian offensive reached farther into France than any other Allied force. More than one million Canadians served in the Army, Navy, and Air Force during the Second World War. More than forty-five thousand of those brave men and women lost their lives.

In the middle of Keith's military service, his parents split up and sold their house in Kerrisdale in Vancouver. Instead of packing up his fragile airplane models, Keith stood at the window of his bedroom and set fire to them one at a time, throwing them out the window for a final doomed flight.

Keith never did become a pilot, though his love of airplanes continued. The entrepreneurial spirit Keith demonstrated in constructing the lemonade stand led him in a different direction. When he returned from his time in the RCAF he started out in construction, but soon he was building houses and selling them. Keith regretted never finishing high school, but he was smart and motivated to succeed even without business training. Over time, his operations grew and he started the Beedie Group, a property development group constructing massive industrial buildings. I met Keith when I interviewed him for a book project about his company. While the story of his business success is interesting, I especially loved hearing Keith talk about his childhood in the war years in Vancouver. The first time he told me how he cut up his dad's movie screen, I laughed out loud. The screen was worth double the money he raised selling lemonade! They were exciting, but difficult times.

Today, the Beedie Group is the largest industrial landowner in Metro Vancouver. Keith's company has built almost one thousand buildings in the Vancouver area. At eighty-five years old, he still goes into work every day. He's come a long way from nailing a movie screen onto a scrap-wood lemonade stand!

Mas Yamamoto, 1943.

The War That Took My Rights Away

Mas Yamamoto, age fourteen
Vancouver, 1942

February, 1942

"Boys and girls, find the home keys with your fingers. Now, begin."

Mrs. Drury, the typing teacher, was standing up at the front of the class. Yet another typing speed test. I didn't need a test to know that I was slow. Really slow.

It was no wonder, really. I had only started typing class right before Christmas break, so I missed the first three months. While everyone else in my class jumped into the exercise with fingers flying, I looked down at my hands and couldn't even remember where to find the first letter.

I didn't know typing but I knew one thing: this class was a total snore compared to cadet training. I sure missed it.

When Japan attacked Pearl Harbor in December, I was horrified along with the rest of the city. I felt the same as everyone else, but after that, not everyone felt the same way about me. I couldn't understand it. Kids I had known my whole life were calling me names. Sure, my last name was Yamamoto, but I was born on the same block as some of those guys. What did I know about bombing Hawaii? Not a darn thing. Now that Canada was at war with Japan, people were acting really strange.

Just before Christmas holidays, and about two weeks after Pearl Harbor, the teacher pulled me out of class for a meeting with the school principal. When I walked into his office, I saw that I was one of about a dozen kids. We were all Japanese Canadians and we were all in the cadets program.

"Children, I am sure this won't come as a big surprise," he began.

Boy, was he ever wrong about that one.

"With things the way they are with the war," he continued, "we had to make a decision about you Japanese students participating in the cadets program. It has to stop, effective immediately. To replace cadets, you will choose between typing class and basketball."

We stood there, too shocked to reply. Then a kid named Jimmy Nakatsu spoke up.

"Sir, both my parents were born in Canada. I am not a Japanese student, I am a Canadian student. What does this have to do with cadets?"

"Son," said the principal, "we just can't be too careful. Cadets is a military program. We are at war with your people now, so precautions need to be taken."

I realized with a jolt that when he talked about "we," he wasn't talking about me. He thought Canada was at war with "my people." I thought my people were Canadian. The twelve of us walked out of the office in silence. I felt numb. What was happening?

That's how I ended up so behind in typing class. My marching formations at cadets were terrific; my typing was not.

Mrs. Drury came up behind me. "Mas, you are going to have to apply yourself more," she said. "Your typing is slow, but you also lose marks for errors. You have five mistakes in that first sentence alone. You should be doing better than that.

I thought your people had strong fine-motor skills."

Who are my people, I wondered? People who live in my neighbourhood, Marpole? Right-handed people? People whose fathers are fishermen? Maybe it is people who wish they were back in cadets instead of stuck in typing class? Deep down, I knew the answer. She meant Japanese people. I was Japanese people.

Maybe I should have signed up for basketball instead.

■ ■ ■

I went straight home after class. I tried not to let my mother know how hard things were getting for me at school. She had enough to worry about. There were seven of us kids and things hadn't been easy for our family. My dad died right before the war started in 1939. We were managing alright, but the last few months since Pearl Harbor had been tough. We were getting strange looks and comments from people on the street. Certainly not from everyone, but from some people I wouldn't have expected. I knew it was uncomfortable for my mother.

When I walked in the front door, I tripped over a box.

"Mom?" I called. "Mom, where are you?"

She popped out of the kitchen. "Mas, you're home," she said. "I could use your help."

"Sure Mom, what can I do?"

"Mrs. Fukushima came by this afternoon and she was talking about the War Measures Act that was passed today. She told me that she heard rumours about Japanese Canadians being affected. She said that we might have to move, just while the war is on."

"Move? Move where?" I asked.

"Just rumours, Mas. But all the same, she suggested that I take a few precautions, just in case."

I was starting to dislike precautions.

"Mrs. Fukushima said that she was giving a few things to her Canadian friends to hold on to. She thought maybe we should do the same."

"Like what, Mom? What kinds of things?"

"Special things, like photographs and such. Things we couldn't replace, or don't want to lose if we are on the move."

This was crazy. Why was my mother talking about moving?

"I have been putting photographs, some dishes, and the silver in boxes. I thought your friends' families might consider putting a box in their attic or basement? Do you think so?"

"Um, maybe," I muttered. I went upstairs to my bedroom and shut the door. I sat on my bed and looked around. My room was full of things that were important to me: trophies, pictures, and scrapbooks. I didn't want to move. The Vancouver I knew had turned upside down. I opened my bag and took out my homework. The city might be going crazy, but I still had math problems to do.

April 1942

Why did I even bother with that homework? It wasn't long before I was pulled out of school altogether. Mrs. Fukushima had been right, but I think even she was surprised how quickly life changed after the War Measures Act was passed. The orders came quickly. The government decided that since Canada was at war with Japan, it was too big a risk to allow people of Japanese heritage to live on the coast. The politicians worried that if Japan invaded, people like me might turn against Canada and fight against Canadians. They thought that we might act as spies and pass on critical defence information to Japan. Families with Japanese names owned one thousand fishing boats in the Vancouver area. The government must have suspected those boats could be turned into a miniature Japanese navy, I guess.

We heard the bad news on March 24th. All Japanese Canadians living with a hundred miles of the Pacific Ocean had twenty-four hours to pack up their belongings before being interned. When I heard the news, I wasn't even sure what interned meant. It turned out to be like prison.

We had little time to prepare before we had to leave for Hastings Park, the gathering point for us. I don't think Hastings Park had very long to prepare for us either. I suppose it wasn't easy to find a place in Vancouver big enough to hold almost eight thousand people on short notice. Hastings Park was a fairground with many agricultural buildings, stables, and barns that were cleaned out quickly. They gave each family one animal stall to live in. The only privacy was a blanket at the end of each stall.

My family got a stall, but I was sent off to a massive dormitory with other boys around my age. It was a big shock to go from our family home to a big room without my mother and brothers and sisters around. My only consolation was that so many of us were in the same situation. Even though we worried about our future in a Vancouver that no longer recognized us as Canadians, we found a lot to distract us. With no school and no chores to do, all we had was time. We found ways to keep busy.

"Mas, meet me behind the latrine in five minutes," said my new friend Doug.

I went to check on my mother, and asked her if there was anything I could do to help her. I knew it wasn't easy for her to keep a bunch of young kids entertained in a barn stall for hours and hours every day. The little ones really didn't understand what was happening to us. They didn't know about politics or anything about the war, just the bits and pieces they could string together from eavesdropping on adults' conversations. Sometimes I envied their lack of understanding. They didn't have questions or hurts, just a few moments of confusion. Not me. I had a lot of time to think about what had forced us to leave our house and our neighbourhood for this place in Hastings Park on the edge of our own city.

My mother told me she didn't need my help so I was free to go. It was sort of funny, I thought. I was free to do what I wanted during the day, but totally captive at the same time. In some ways, with no school to worry about and no chores to do, I was having the time of my life with my friends.

It wasn't until I was on my way to meet Doug that I started to wonder why on earth he chose the latrine. There were a million places around here, so why would we meet at the bathroom? Maybe I didn't hear him right.

I turned the corner and saw five guys huddled around the back wall of the latrine. So, I was in the right place, but I still didn't know what I was doing there.

"What's up, boys?" I asked.

"What took you so long, Mas?" Doug asked.

"Nothing," I said.

Doug was holding a roll of toilet paper.

"Answering nature's call?"

"What? No! I wouldn't . . . I . . . that's not . . ." I stumbled.

"No, Mas," said Jim Nakamura. "This one isn't for wiping, it's for lighting."

"Lighting? What do you mean?"

He pulled out a box of matches. "We're going to light these rolls on fire and then lob them down the row of toilets. The fellows in there doing their business will be shocked out of their shorts!"

No kidding. I had to laugh. What would I do if a flaming roll of toilet paper rolled through my toilet? I was happy that I wasn't on the receiving end of this trick.

We clustered around and distributed the matches and the toilet paper rolls. It was like a military attack. I guess we were missing the cadets program. We sneaked around the side of the building, ammunition in hand. When we were outside the main door, we waited for the signal.

"Three, two, one . . ." whispered Jim.

We all lit our matches on the bottoms of our shoes and held the flames to the edges of the toilet paper rolls. They caught on fire quickly. It was a bit like a live grenade; you didn't want to hold on too long. We opened the latrine door and all six of us simultaneously sent the rolls flying down the trough that ran through the middle of the toilets.

As soon as I heard the shrieks, I turned to run. I was laughing so hard! Some of those screams didn't sound too manly to me!

As the six of us sprinted away, the protests and shouts grew louder. I wasn't going to stick around!

This wasn't what I expected to be doing on a spring day. I was joking with my friends, getting into just the kind of mischief that I would have avoided at home for fear of getting in trouble. Here, it didn't seem to matter. It was fun and harmless, I figured. And a lot more fun than typing class. I had a feeling that I should take fun where I found it. I had no idea what would be coming next.

What do we know for sure?

Here's an interesting coincidence: Mas Yamamoto, the boy in this story, and Keith Beedie, from the previous story in this book, attended the same Vancouver school, Point Grey Junior High. Keith raised money for the Air Supremacy Drive, and Mas told me that he remembers his mother sending him to school with twenty-five cents to buy War Savings Stamps to support the Canadian war effort.

Both boys took part in the cadets program. They were very much alike in their interests and way of life except that one had a Japanese family name. Two Vancouver kids; two very different experiences of the Second World War.

More than twenty-two thousand Japanese Canadians from British Columbia were interned during the Second World War; fourteen thousand of them had been born in Canada.

After a few months at Hastings Park, the federal government sent Mas and his family to the Lemon Creek internment camp in the Interior of British Columbia. It's hard to tell from the words *camp* and *internment,* but there was nothing fun or voluntary about these locations. They were effectively prisons. Families were given wooden shacks to live in, two families per building. Although it was an improvement over Hastings Park, the camp was primitive and poorly organized.

To this day, Mas is an amazingly positive person. Despite the injustice he and his family suffered when they were removed from their home and sent away against their wishes, he is still able to remember his time in Lemon Creek without bitterness.

The Japanese Canadians who were removed from the Coast had a long, hard journey ahead of them. You might think that their troubles ended with the conclusion of the war, but they didn't. Anti-Japanese sentiment didn't decrease with Japan's surrender in 1945. In 1946, there was an organized effort to have all people of Japanese descent removed from British Columbia for good. Japanese Canadians were told to move east of the Rocky Mountains, or be shipped to Japan. For many families, this forced migration caused terrible pain as people scrambled to find places to stay, losing touch and drifting apart.

It wasn't only family relationships that suffered. Mas had some schooling at Lemon Creek, but by the time the restrictions on Japanese Canadians were lifted, he was twenty years old and hadn't finished high school. A dedicated student before the war, Mas did not expect to be in that position at that age. It was another hardship visited upon him by the injustice of the internment.

Japanese Canadians weren't legally permitted back to the Vancouver area or permitted to vote until 1949, four years after the end of the Second World War. Not everyone returned home. Some families stayed where they had made new lives. Sadly, there was another big shock in store. When the government sent Japanese Canadians away, it seized all of their possessions: houses, property, businesses, cars, boats, and any other assets that could be taken. Everything was supposed to be held in trust, and given back when they returned. Instead, the government sold everything. When the families finally returned to the coast, all of their belongings were gone. Possessions and assets that had taken years and sometimes generations to acquire disappeared. It was devastating for them. Mas was an adult of twenty-two by 1949. Although disadvantaged by his lack of formal education, he was determined not to let it hold him back. He earned his high school diploma while working, then applied to university. He would eventually earn his PHD in pharmacology in between working, marrying, and raising a family in North Vancouver.

In 1988, the Canadian government made a formal apology to the Japanese Canadians who had been interned. The government then offered to pay each surviving internee a lump sum of twenty-one thousand dollars as partial compensation for their hardship. Many people believe that Joy Kogawa's book *Obasan* played a role in the government's decision to apologize and pay reparations. *Obasan* is about Japanese Canadian internment through the eyes of a young girl. It is a fantastic book. If you haven't read it, find it in your local bookstore or school library.

There is an interesting footnote to this story. Mas Yamamoto may have had to wait until 1949 to be allowed to vote, but exactly sixty years later, his daughter Naomi Yamamoto was elected as Member of the Legislative Assembly for North Vancouver-Lonsdale and appointed as a cabinet minister. I learned about Mas when I read an article about his family's incredible story in a newsletter. I was really interested in their journey from internment to politics. In the article, he described the ups and downs from the time his family spent interned and displaced. The mistreatment of Japanese Canadians represents a truly shameful part of Canada's history, yet the Yamamotos offer an amazing example of how to move forward. Despite the suffering they endured at the hands of a wartime government, they didn't give up on Canada. Now Naomi Yamamoto is a part of our government, making sure such tragedies never occur again.

Dawnne Blaker in front of her house on Pender Street.
BLAKER FAMILY COLLECTION

Nickels on Pender Street

Dawnne Blaker, age eight
East Vancouver, 1954

"Peter," I called. "Mustache Man!"

The sun was dipping in the sky. It was almost time to meet the Mustache Man. In the evenings, we'd run down to the end of our block to find the Mustache Man as he walked home from work.

"A nickel, a nickel," we'd chant.

If he'd had a good day, he'd jingle the coins in his pocket and pull out a nickel to reward us for accompanying him the rest of the way home. Some days we got nothing, but most days we did.

A shiny coin meant one thing in our world: candy. Knowing that we had a bit of money made us feel powerful. Our parents talked about money all the time: how much they had, how much they needed, how much things cost, how quickly it disappeared. We knew we had to enjoy our money while we had it.

After school, the same group of us played together every day: Peter and Ivan, who were brothers; Noreen and Rae, who were sisters; and me. My brothers were much older than me. They either ignored me, or tickled me so hard it brought tears to my eyes, but mostly we avoided each other.

Unlike the other Chinese Canadian kids in my class at Strathcona Elementary, I came straight home after school. I didn't go to the Chinese school across the street when the final bell rang. I watched the others trudge over, shoulders slumped and feet dragging. It was tough in there. I heard kids talking all the time about getting in trouble, getting caned and rapped on the knuckles for misbehaving. I got in enough trouble in regular school. My knuckles would be raw if I had to go over there.

Instead I ran home to play. I had to hurry because my parents worried about me walking by myself. It was a pretty tough neighbourhood where we lived. There were lots of places for a kid to get in a mess.

When I arrived at our place, I ran straight inside to see my mother. She wasn't healthy. She spent every day lying down on a cot that stayed in our kitchen. I'd let her know I was home safe, then head out to find my friends. We often played in the fort we'd built out of an old oil barrel in the backyard, but today Peter, Ivan, Noreen, Rae, and I were goofing around out front.

"The Mustache Man came home early today," Peter said. "He was sick."

No candy for us today. Darn it.

Peter and Ivan's mother came out their front door and shouted for them in Russian.

"Twenty minutes until we have to go in for dinner," Peter told us. "Want to play a quick game of Hide and Seek?"

"Sure," I said. "Who is It?

"I'll go," said Rae.

Just as we were discussing the rules and boundaries, we stopped. We could hear shouts and loud laughter coming from around the corner on Campbell Avenue. We knew that laughter. Uh oh, I thought.

Five kids appeared on bikes. They sped up close to our group, then skidded to a stop at the last second, just before hitting us. We knew these kids, the meanest in the neighbourhood. They didn't play after school. They just rode around looking for trouble. If they couldn't find any, they made their own. We'd had problems with them before.

"Well, if it isn't the Pender Street babies," sneered Deb, the biggest girl.

"Keefer Street kids," whispered Rae, beside me. She sounded scared. I was too.

"This street is such a dump," said John, throwing down his bike. What a laugh. Our street was no different than theirs.

"Yeah," agreed Deb. "It's filthy over here." She kicked at some trash on the sidewalk.

"If it's so bad, why don't you go home?" asked Ivan.

"We will," said Deb. "Believe me, we don't want to hang out here. As soon as you pay us, we'll go."

"Pay you?" I asked. "What for?" My friends and I looked at each other uneasily. What were these Keefer Street kids talking about?

"Well, if you babies want to play here," said Deb, "and I have no idea why you would want to, you have to pay us a nickel each."

"We aren't paying you," said Peter. "This is our street. We'll play here if we want."

I glanced around to see if there were any adults around, but the street was deserted except for the ten of us.

"Pay up," Deb said, off her bike now too. "You don't want to find out what happens if you say no."

I took a deep breath. "I don't have a nickel to pay you and even if I did, I still wouldn't give it up," I said. I looked over to my friends and saw that they looked just as defiant as I felt. Those Keefer Street kids were mean all right, but we Pender kids weren't pushovers.

On the outside, I knew I looked shy. When I was younger, my father used to take me for walks through Chinatown on his days off. As we walked along the sidewalk, shopkeepers came out to greet us. Everyone knew my father and his shy little daughter. They tried everything to get me to do little tricks, or sing a song, or even just talk. It never worked. Their offers of fresh slices of *char siu* were all refused. I wasn't going to be bought off by a measly piece of pork.

I wasn't the loudest, most outspoken kid, but I wasn't going to let anyone take advantage of me. Not shopkeepers, and not neighbourhood bullies on bikes.

Deb looked me up and down. "You sure?" she asked.

I nodded.

"You babies too?" she asked my friends.

They nodded as well.

The Keefer Street kids seemed a bit thrown off. I laughed a little bit, because I realized they didn't know what to do. Deb told us we didn't want to know what happened if we didn't pay. That's because she didn't know what happened if we didn't pay!

We all stood there, a bit awkwardly. The Keefer kids started whispering to each other.

"Maybe we should run home?" Noreen whispered to me.

"Or just run anywhere?" added her sister Rae, the littlest of us all.

I looked at Peter and Ivan. They looked determined to stand their ground. So was I.

Dawnne with her father.

"If we run this time, they'll just come back," I whispered.

"We're not running," stated Peter, not even bothering to whisper.

"Then I will make you run," shouted Deb. She went over to the empty lot across the street and grabbed something from the ground, then came rushing back towards us. She had a two-by-four piece of wood in her hand.

We were too shocked to move. She was almost on top of us before we realized what was happening. Deb ran right for Rae. She was the smallest, an easy target.

Peter tried to head her off before she got to Rae, but Deb was fast and she'd surprised us with this attack. She swung at Rae before Peter reached them.

We watched the piece of wood swing up high and arc through the air. Deb brought it down hard, right across little Rae's arm.

We heard the crack. The sound of Rae's arm snapping must have shocked Deb too. She froze for a second, then dropped the wood and ran back to her bike. The Keefer Street kids hadn't moved a muscle since Deb picked up the wood. Now they scrambled to get back on their bikes.

Rae dropped to the ground without a sound. Peter ran after Deb.

"Come back here," he yelled. "Come back and fight someone your own size, coward."

It was too late. Deb mounted her bike and pedalled around the corner, the rest of her gang trailing behind her. I could hear her laughing. Her laughter made me furious.

Noreen crouched over Rae, who was sobbing now. Ivan ran inside to get the sisters' mother.

"Why'd she have to hit Rae?" I asked Peter as he walked back, out of breath from chasing Deb.

"Easy," he told me. "Because she could."

What do we know for sure?

Rae's arm was broken in two places. She was taken to the hospital and her arm was put in a cast. Even though everyone knew who was responsible, nothing happened to Deb.

I met Dawnne Blaker years ago because she is my mother's hairdresser. I knew she grew up on the Downtown Eastside, so I asked her about her childhood for this book. I was amazed at her experiences. She couldn't remember the names of some of the kids in this story, so I gave them names, but the details are all true—including Rae's broken arm.

Dawnne remembers incidents like this one happening frequently in her neighbourhood. She told me that her parents and her friends' parents were too busy working hard to make ends meet to worry about their kids' squabbles.

Chinatown and the rest of the Downtown Eastside has had a long turbulent history in Vancouver. At the turn of the twentieth century, the area was the centre of town, and home to offices, public buildings, and commerce. Over the years, as Vancouver development moved west, the Downtown Eastside entered a decline. Families like Dawnne's no longer felt safe and many people moved out of the area, which meant it deteriorated even further. While Chinatown maintained a strong and active community, poverty and crime took hold in the larger community. Recently, residents of the area have worked hard to make the Downtown Eastside a place where families feel secure again. The revitalization of the neighbourhoods in the area continues today. A really fun way to see Chinatown is a visit to the night market in the summertime. Or check out the Vancouver Chinatown Festival, which usually takes place in August.

Both of Dawnne's parents were born in Vancouver, but they raised their kids in a traditional Chinese home. Her father was a bricklayer and construction worker. Her mother was ill with a severe chronic illness, leaving her bedridden for Dawnne's entire childhood. Life at home was stressful and often lonely. She says that her older brothers were often away and took virtually no interest in her, her father was working as much as possible, and her mother was immobile. Life wasn't easy, but Dawnne found her own strength. She told me that "you can take the girl out of East Vancouver, but you can't take East Vancouver out of the girl."

When Dawnne was ten, her family moved to Burnaby because her father believed that life would be better for her there. Ten days after the move, her mother passed away unexpectedly. Dawnne was shocked. While she knew that her mother was ill, she wasn't prepared for the possibility that she could die. It wasn't a good start in a new city.

Dawnne found herself at a school in Burnaby where she was one of only three Asian Canadian students. She missed the diversity of her old neighbourhood and the friends she had left behind. Her father remarried when she was twelve and had another daughter when she was seventeen. Although she had lost touch with her old friends, Dawnne moved back to the Downtown Eastside as soon as she possibly could. She'd had some tough experiences in her ten years there, but it was where she felt she belonged. Dawnne grew up to have a daughter of her own and today she works in Vancouver as a hairdresser.

The incident in this story could have happened in any neighbourhood. For as long as there've been kids, there's been bullying, but there is no time or place when it is okay. Dawnne felt that there was no place for her or her friends to turn to for help. She stood up to Deb in the story, but Rae got hurt. Sometimes, kids need some adult help. Today, there are numerous ways that kids can deal with bullying before it gets out of hand and someone gets hurt. If you or someone you know is dealing with a bully, you can talk to a family member, teacher, friend, or school counsellor about it, or you can call the Kids Help Phone at any time of the day or night: 1-800-668-6868.

Judy's passport photo, taken to come to Canada.
BAU FAMILY COLLECTION

Just Concentrate

Judy Bau, age seven
Vancouver, 1971

"Wait for me," my sister Ann shouted from behind me. "I want to tell Mama too. Judy, wait!"

I was too excited to wait for her. I ran across our front lawn and cut the corner to go around to the back entrance of our basement suite. I burst through the door, blurting out our news before Ann had even reached the backyard.

"A field trip, Mama . . . with the school!" I dropped to the floor and started pulling everything out of my school bag until I found the piece of paper that our teacher had handed to us. "You put your name at the bottom of this paper, Mama," I told her. "Then we can go."

Behind me, Ann arrived and threw her school bag on the kitchen floor. "That is not fair, you run faster," she said. "I wanted to tell her."

This was going to be the most exciting thing that had happened in the three weeks we'd been in school in Vancouver: a class outing to the Stanley Park zoo. At least it sounded exciting the way that our resource teacher had explained it. Ann and I were starting to understand the words that our teachers and classmates were speaking to us. Three weeks ago, all I knew in English was my name and the alphabet.

Lord Nelson Elementary was a different world from my old school in Taipei, Taiwan. There I had been top of my class, the first to finish everything. I loved being the quickest. Not here, not anymore. It is impossible to feel smart when you don't speak the language. My sister and I were trying our best to catch up, but English was hard.

When we stepped off the airplane on Victoria Day, three weeks ago, I was shocked by the wide open spaces and white faces we saw. Vancouver was so bright and sunny and it wasn't crowded like Taipei. We drove to our new home. I felt disappointed that although Vancouver was big and bright, inside our place was dark and cramped.

Two days later, we walked with our papa to our new school. We had brushed our hair until it shone and our clothes were spotless. Papa went into the school office, while we stood outside and watched the other kids enter the school, laughing and playing.

Papa came out and told us that we would be going to the same Grade One classroom, even though Ann was younger than me and should have been in Kindergarten. It was better for us to stay together, he told us, since we would have only six weeks in class before school let out for the summer. We should try our best to learn English, he said, and try our best to fit in.

We walked away from the big school building, towards a smaller building in the middle of the field. It was a portable, I found out later. Papa walked us to the door and knocked. He spoke to the teacher and pointed to us. The teacher beckoned to us to come inside. My chin started to quiver. I could feel the tears welling up in my eyes and I tried to brush them away, but more came behind them. I looked over at Ann and saw that she too was crying.

Our papa kept speaking to the teacher while she kept the door open and motioned for him to stay outside. He kept talking and she kept gently pointing outside again. He leaned down. "Be very good girls and listen to your teacher," he said, turning to leave.

The teacher shut the door firmly behind him. He was gone. Part of me wanted to be strong for my papa and my sister, but another part of me couldn't believe he had left us. He had abandoned us in this strange place with all these faces looking at us like we were aliens.

The teacher said a bunch of words. I didn't know what she wanted from us. Funny sounds tumbled out of her mouth, but they meant nothing to me. She pointed to seats and we sat in them.

I think I cried the entire first day of school.

The next day was a little better. And the one after that too.

We started going to a little classroom, just Ann and me, for a couple of hours every day. Mrs. Delaney spoke slowly and used pictures to teach us new words. She taught us about Canada and introduced us to new words every day.

We ate lunch with her, trying out Canadian foods that tasted foreign and strange. Some flavours were too odd to enjoy, like the funny sour taste of tomato soup. It looked so beautiful and red, but I didn't like the tart flavor on my tongue. The crackers that came with the soup were terrific—crunchy and salty.

Our first three weeks at school were just like the tomato soup and crackers. Some experiences were too new and strange to be pleasant, but others were surprising and wonderful. The thought of a field trip to a zoo was very, very wonderful.

"Mrs. Delaney told us that we need to pack a lunch to take with us, Mama," I went on, waving the permission slip in front of her.

Judy, Ann, and Sandy Bau at Stanley Park.
BAU FAMILY COLLECTION

Ann had her piece of paper out now too. Mama laughed and picked up our little sister, Sandy, from the floor, away from our stomping, excited feet. She took my paper out of my hand and looked at it. Her face looked just like my face at school, examining the weird squiggles written there, wishing they made sense.

"Show me where I put my name," she said. Ann and I looked at the paper. We both shrugged.

In the ten days we had to wait for the field trip, Ann and I became spies. At recess and lunchtime, we studied our classmates and their foods. What mysterious things did they eat? What was a Canadian lunch? Each day, we came home from school with fresh instructions for our mother.

"The sandwich should be between slices of white bread," I instructed. "Snowy white bread."

"And we need something sweet, like a cookie or candy," Ann added.

"In a lunch bag made of brown paper," I said.

Our mother listened patiently to our ever-changing requests, then made a trip to the grocery store and did her best to make sense of our instructions. When the big day finally arrived, Ann and I were bursting with excitement. We arrived at school, confident that we were carrying authentic Canadian lunches. Our English was improving. I didn't think we stuck out as the new girls quite as much as we did when we first arrived. School was hard for me because I stuck out enough for another reason. I was tall. In Taipei, kids used to tease me and call me Giraffe, Daddy Long Legs, and other nasty names. In Vancouver, I was in a lower grade so that I could be with my sister, so I was even taller compared to my classmates. I didn't need anything else to make me feel different.

When the bus arrived to take us to Stanley Park, Ann and I climbed in with all the other kids. I couldn't wait to get to the zoo and see the animals. I couldn't wait to pull out my lunch. Everything was perfect. We were blending in, just as we'd planned.

We loved our morning at the zoo. Our new friends helped us learn the names of the animals. We even taught them some animal names in Chinese. We laughed because the sounds that we say animals make—cows *moo*, for example, and chickens *cluck*—are different in Chinese and English, which is funny, because the animals don't speak either language. After we had explored the whole zoo, it was time for lunch.

"Come on, Ann," I told my sister, pulling on her arm so we could sit together. "How about here?" We plunked down next to big group of girls from our class. "Can we sit here?" I asked them in English. The girls nodded and giggled. Perfect.

Ann and I began unloading our lunch from our bags, sneaking peeks out of the corners of our eyes to see how our food compared to the others. So far, so good. The only difference was that our mother had packed our brown paper bags inside a plastic grocery bag to protect them from rain damage. It didn't matter. It was close enough.

I laid everything out. Our mother had done a wonderful job. She had even cut our sandwiches on a diagonal. Our two little apples, our cookies, even our little, round containers of juice were perfect.

Ann and I smiled at each other. I felt a little bit guilty about asking so much of our mother, since she had a lot to adjust to herself, but she wanted so much to help us fit in that she insisted it was okay. I felt so lucky.

While Ann bit into her sandwich, I set about opening up our juice containers. I picked up the small, round can. I looked at it. There was no obvious way to open it. I flipped it over to see if the other side would reveal an opening. Nothing.

I took a quick look around to see if any of the other kids had the same type of juice. They didn't. I nudged Ann. She shrugged.

The top was a metal lid. I tried to pry it off. When that didn't work, I tried to pull at it with my teeth. That couldn't be right, I thought.

I sighed. After all this preparation, now I was going to have to ask for help. Before going up to the teacher, I thought about the English words I would need. With the sentence running through my head, I walked up to Mrs. Watt.

"Mrs. Watt," I began. "Help, please?" I said in English.

"Certainly, Judy," said Mrs. Watt. "What can I do?"

"My juice . . ." I said.

Mrs. Watt took the juice from my hand. She looked at the can, looked at the white tape running around the bottom of the metal lid, then read the label.

"Oh, honey," she said. "This isn't good juice for you."

"Not good?" I echoed.

"This is juice *concentrate*, Judy. You pour out this juice into a big container and add lots of water. You can't drink it without water. No good."

"No good . . ." I repeated.

I hated not understanding. All I got from what Mrs. Watt said was that the juice was no good. I had no idea why. Add water? What did that mean?

Mrs. Watt must have seen the confusion on my face. She tried to explain again. She pulled the white tape off and took off the lid. Well, at least that solved the mystery of how to open it.

"Try it," she said.

I did. It was awful. Sweet and sour at the same time. I understood now. My shoulders slumped. I took the can out of Mrs. Watt's hand and said thank you. I walked back to where Ann was sitting all alone, looking confused.

"It's no good," I told her in Chinese. "We can't drink it." I took hers out of her hand, too. I walked over to the garbage can and threw them both away.

"Why?" Ann asked me as I sat back down.

"I think Mama made a mistake and bought us something that makes juice but this isn't juice right now," I said. I felt like everyone was looking at us. Were those whispers? I could hear laughter and I wondered if it was directed at us. I could feel tears in my eyes. They were never far away since we had moved to Canada.

Suddenly, I felt a hand on my shoulder. I looked up to see Mrs. Watt.

"Ann, Judy, come with me, girls," she said.

Ann and I stood up and walked with our teacher to a nearby concession stand.

"Two 7 Ups, please," she told the person behind the counter. She pulled out her wallet to pay, then handed us two big cups with straws in them. Ann and I looked at each other and put the straws in our mouths. I took a drink.

It was delicious. It was cold, sweet, and it tickled my tongue.

What do we know for sure?

Judy and Ann Bau will never forget their first day at school in Canada, but they found out much later that they weren't the only ones who struggled that morning. Their father, Paul, had a tough time too. Dropping Judy and Ann off at the classroom door was just as difficult for him as it was for his daughters. He spoke English fairly well, but he knew how limited the girls were in their ability to communicate. When he was talking to the teacher, he suggested that maybe he should stay. The teacher insisted that he leave, and let the sisters adjust on their own. He found it painful to turn away from his crying daughters.

Judy remembers feeling hurt and alone when her father left. Years later, Judy and Ann found out that he hadn't left.

He stood outside the window of the portable classroom and watched his daughters crying at their desks. He stayed there for half an hour, tears running down his own face. Their father believed strongly that he was offering them the best opportunity available, but that didn't make it easy.

The Bau family had only a few hundred dollars when they moved to Vancouver. They had no relatives, friends, or connections in the city. Like many families who come to Canada to make a new life, they had to start from scratch.

While Judy and Ann struggled to find their place in school, their father found work to support the family. He took a job at a Midas shop working on cars. When all three girls were in school, their mother cleaned rooms and worked in a food processing plant. Judy remembers all three sisters taking turns massaging their mother's sore hands after she had worked all day.

When school ended for the summer that first year, Judy and Ann played outside every day with the kids in their neighbourhood. By the time they returned to school in September, they could speak much better English and they settled in more easily. Judy moved up a grade and quickly went back to being a strong student. In fact, it didn't take long for Judy's parents to complain that she had become so comfortable in English that she needed to go to Chinese school to maintain her first language. She says her experience as the new kid in class made her more understanding when other newcomers arrived. She made friends with many students who were new to Canada.

Thanks to a lot of hard work and saving, the Bau family was able to buy a house within two years of moving to Vancouver. Judy's dad got a good job at a Chrysler dealership and the three sisters attended Charles Dickens Annex elementary school, which they loved. Despite the terrible sadness of losing their mother in 1981, the three Bau sisters grew up as happy Vancouver kids.

I met Judy through her youngest sister, Sandy, who is a friend of mine. I mentioned to Sandy that I was working on this book and she told me her family's story of coming to Canada and adjusting to life in Vancouver. She was so little that she didn't remember much, but she recommended that I talk to Judy. I am so glad I did.

Judy graduated from Sir Charles Tupper High School and attended the University of British Columbia to earn a liberal arts degree. After years in graphic design, today she works as a freelance copywriter. All three Bau sisters, Judy, Ann, and Sandy, still live in Vancouver. Judy still doesn't care for tomato soup.

Bira.

Going Out for the Team

Bira Bindra, age twelve
Steveston, 1977

I see the pass coming. I run towards the soccer ball. Perfect!

I sprint for the goal. Wet grass is flying out behind me. I make a move on the keeper. I can see him start to dive to the right, but he isn't committed yet. I wait for a moment until he's going right for sure. I wind up and kick the soccer ball as hard as I can, aiming for the left side of the net. As soon as it leaves my foot, I know it's going in.

The ball sails into the goal.

I run back to my teammates for high-fives all around. I feel fantastic.

Six months ago, it was a different story. I didn't play soccer and the teammates giving me high-fives for my goal weren't my friends.

Thank goodness for sports.

■ ■ ■

I looked out my classroom window. I saw a big group of kids on the grass field and I could see more coming. I didn't know what to do.

This whole mess started yesterday. I get so sick of kids making stupid comments to me about being from India, or having brown skin. I try my best to ignore them, but they know how much it bugs me. They keep at it until I snap. I feel the anger filling me up inside. When it gets to be too much, there's nowhere for it to go but out.

The next thing I know, I'm in a fight

Once or twice a week, I end up in the principal's office for fighting. He's alright, though. He always asks me the same question—what did they say to me this time? He knows it isn't easy being the only Indo-Canadian kid in school. He gets angry with the kids who call me names, but he also talks to me about controlling my temper.

Easier said than done.

Yesterday, it was more of the same. Some dumb kid running off at the mouth, and saying all kinds of stuff to make me mad. I hit him. I felt it coming and I tried to stop it, but I couldn't.

"You're dead, Bira," he yelled at me from the floor. "My brother is in high school and he and his friends are coming tomorrow. They're gonna beat you up." He was crying a bit. His friends helped him up, but he was mad. He pushed them away and shouted at me, "You're gonna get it, Bira."

This morning, all the kids were talking about the fight after school today.

Great. Now what? I sort of hoped that maybe those high school kids would have something better to do after school than come over here and beat up a kid they don't even know. No such luck. When I looked out the window again, there was no mistaking the high school boys crowded around Dan: his brother and his friends.

Should I go find the principal, I wondered? I knew how that would turn out. He'd march out across the field and tell off those kids. I wouldn't have to fight, but then everyone would know that I sent him.

I walked through the big double doors and walked over to

the big group. As I was walking, I could hear the chant starting.

"Fight! Fight! Fight! Fight!"

As I got closer, the crowd parted and made a big circle around me. The circle closed up behind me, so I was stuck inside. As I stood there, another kid stepped into the middle of the circle with me. I looked at him. I had never seen this kid before in my life. He was some high school guy who had no idea who I was either. What was I doing fighting him?

"Hey, I hear you like to fight," the kid across from me said. I shrugged.

He ran at me. I stepped to one side and came at him. Punches were flying, and as usual, I was winning. I was a big kid; tall and strong. Good thing too. I hated to think how much harder life would be if I couldn't fight back.

The fight was over pretty fast. He went down and didn't want to get up again. I turned around to leave and the circle parted for me. I walked away, back into the school to get my things and go home.

Just another day at school.

■ ■ ■

The next day at recess, I played soccer. That was one way to avoid trouble with other kids. It was mostly the same boys who played every day. As soon as the bell rang, they bolted onto the field and played until the next bell rang to go back. That didn't leave a lot of time for name-calling or stupid comments.

My friend Scott had showed me how to play earlier in the year. Before that, I'd never touched a soccer ball. Heck, I'd never even seen one.

There were a lot of things like that, stuff I'd never seen before coming to Canada. When we moved here from India, three years ago, everything was brand new. Kids would laugh if they knew so I didn't talk about it, but before we came here I'd never seen a television or ridden in a car. They were too busy making fun of me to really know me. They didn't know that when I arrived in Vancouver at nine years old, I had worked twelve hours every day on a farm for almost a year before starting school. School was something brand new too. I didn't go to school in the Punjab. Instead, I stayed home with my grandfather. He was still in India and I missed him all the time.

I kicked the soccer ball around with the others. The funny thing was that I was pretty good at it. Scott told me that he and most of his friends had been playing soccer since kindergarten. Once I learned all the rules and played for a few months, I was just as good a soccer player as they were.

"Bira, over here," shouted a kid named Kyle. I passed him the ball. He ran towards the opposite goal, marked by two guys' sweatshirts tossed on the ground. He passed a couple of other kids, then fired the ball back to me. I was running full speed. Without stopping, I shot the ball right at the goal. It soared over the right shoulder of the keeper.

"Score . . . !" shouted Kyle.

We kept playing for another ten minutes until recess was over. I scored three more times.

As we were running back to class, Scott came up beside me.

"Hey Bira, we've got tryouts coming up for my soccer team next week," he said. "You should come out."

"I don't know," I said. "What do you do?"

"If you make the team, there are practices during the week and games on the weekend," he said. "It's fun. You're a really good player, you'll make it for sure."

"I don't know. I'll think about," I told him.

After school that day, I went home and mentioned the soccer team tryouts to my parents.

"Bira, why did we bring you thousands of miles to this country? Not so you could just play games," my father told me.

"You should focus on your studies," said my mother. "We don't have time to take you to all those games and practices."

"I could get there myself on my bike, or go with a friend," I said. Once I started explaining it to my parents, I realized how much I wanted to play. I felt good when I played sports. On the field, I felt like I had friends. I wasn't great at schoolwork, so school wasn't much fun, but when I played sports I was strong. I felt like I belonged.

"Don't let it get in the way of school," said my mother. My father just nodded. So that was it. I could try out.

Scott and I rode our bikes to the tryout on the following Saturday. As soon as we got there, I realized that all the other kids had special soccer shoes on with cleats on the bottom. I just had my regular shoes. They were wearing soccer jerseys and soccer shorts. They even had shin guards. I just had shins.

The coaches showed us drills and things to practise. We played mini-games and they were really fun. It didn't matter that my shoes were wrong, or that I didn't have the right equipment, I was just as good as the other kids.

"What's your name, kid?" asked one of the coaches during a drill.

"Bira," I told him.

"Bira, huh? Well, Bira, do you want to play on our team?"

"I guess so," I said.

"Happy to have you, son," he said, patting me on the shoulder. I looked over at Scott, and he gave me the signal. Thumbs-up.

■ ■ ■

I looked forward to practices and games more than anything. My parents still weren't excited about me playing. When I asked them for money for the deposit on my soccer uniform, they said no. When I told my coach I didn't have it, he told me not to worry about a deposit.

Almost right away, I was the leading scorer on our team. Getting goals was a good feeling, but I really just loved playing.

I was getting better too. I could tell that I was improving. Pretty soon, recesses and lunch hour were different. Instead of hearing taunts and nasty words, I heard my name used a new way.

"Let's pick teams," they'd say.

"I'll take Bira."

"You got Bira last time, we get him this recess."

"I get to pick first and I pick Bira."

"That's not fair."

It was the beginning of a fight, but boy, did it ever feel different.

What do we know for sure?

Bira Bindra told me that the fight with the high school kid was the last one he ever fought. It happened at around the same time that he found success with sports, which changed everything.

He was a great athlete and that was all it took for the kids in his school to start seeing him differently.

After a couple of tough years getting teased and bullied, playing sports helped Bira make friends in elementary school that he still has today. It is incredible how one simple thing like sports could give Bira an outlet for his frustrations and a new confidence in himself. It also helped other kids see him in a new light.

Despite the huge positive influence that sports had in Bira's life, his parents didn't see their value at first. They had sacrificed a lot to come to Canada and they wanted Bira to focus on his school work. What they didn't know was that some of the best opportunities of Bira's life would come through sports. Later in his life, his parents told him that they were happy he persevered with athletics even though he didn't get much support from them at the time.

School never came easily to Bira. When he arrived in Canada from the Punjab in 1974, he was nine years old. He hadn't attended school in India because the nearest school was too far from his village. Instead of starting Grade Four, he spent almost a year working in the fields. He went out to Abbotsford with his mother by truck at 6:30 every morning, and then worked until dark before heading home to sleep. The next morning, they'd get up and do it again.

For many immigrant families coming to British Columbia from the state of Punjab in India, farming is a logical occupation. The Punjab is called the bread basket of India. It has some of the most fertile soil in the world. Instead of the rice, wheat, and cotton grown in the Punjab, most BC crops are fruits and vegetables. The farmers need to adjust their practices for the different crops, but they bring their agricultural skills to our province's harvest.

Bira had a lot of catching up to do when he started school for the first time in his life at ten years old, but he told me that he didn't feel like he fit in until he started playing sports. Before long, other kids were trying to catch up to him.

Bira's competitive spirit took him a long way in athletics. He switched from soccer to basketball in Grade Nine. With hard work and good coaching he went from absolute beginner to captain of his high school team in Grades Eleven and Twelve. When he was in Grade Twelve, his high school team, Steveston Secondary School, became BC provincial champions. The night of the final, his best friend's parents went to Bira's house to pick up his parents and bring them to the game. They had never watched basketball before. Though they struggled to understand the game, Bira impressed them.

Bira went on to play college and university basketball. He also co-founded the popular Dolphin Park basketball tournament held in Richmond every summer.

In the last three decades, India has been one of the top sources of immigration to BC, along with China, Taiwan, and Hong Kong. Between 1980 and 2000, more than seventy-seven thousand Indian immigrants landed in BC, representing twelve per cent of all immigration to the province. Most settled in the Lower Mainland.

Bira credits those tough early days of elementary school with teaching him two things. The first is that playing sports can have a huge positive influence on a kid's life. The second was the importance of staying true to who he was as a person and not pretending to be anyone else.

Today, Bira is a professional firefighter in White Rock. He was the first Indo-Canadian hired by the fire department. He told me that at first he was a bit worried about fitting in, but within his first year of being hired, he had his crew drinking chai tea instead of coffee.

Bira and his wife are raising their three daughters to believe in the positive power of sports in their lives. His life is a great example of how true that is.

Eric with Expo Ernie, 1986.

Never Eat Ice Cream Before Hamburgers

Eric Butler, age twelve
Vancouver, 1986

I woke up ten minutes before my alarm was supposed to go off. I'd set it for seven o'clock to be sure that I could squeeze every possible minute out of the day. I had big plans: Expo '86, by myself, without my parents, for the first time ever.

I jumped out of bed and pulled on the clothes that I had laid out on my desk chair the night before. No time to waste.

I opened the drawer in my bedside table and pulled out my wallet. I checked the contents for the hundredth time. I dumped the money out on my bed and quadruple-checked that I had enough.

Bus fare? Check.

Money for my all-day ride pass? Check.

Lunch money? Check.

I'd been saving all of my babysitting earnings for a couple of weeks. My family had been to Expo a bunch of times since it opened in May, but I had never gone on my own and I had never gone on the rides. When I asked my mom if I could go with a friend, and she said yes, I was so happy that I thought I might explode. I had been eyeing those rides for weeks. The Looping Starship, the Scream Machine, the Cariboo Log Chute, and the scariest ride of all, the parachutes.

I scooped up the money from my bed and put it back in my wallet. I was good to go. After a quick bowl of cereal, I got ready and called my friend Mike. We agreed to meet at the east gate of the Expo lands at ten.

"Eric, stick with Mike and make sure you keep enough money to catch the bus home," my mom told me when I said goodbye. "Be careful."

"Okay, see you later," I shouted on my way out the door.

I had never taken the bus downtown by myself before. I got to my stop just as the bus was pulling up. As soon as I was on board, I felt a huge smile spread across my face. I was completely free. I had money in my wallet and a whole day wide open for fun.

In fact, getting to Expo was part of the fun. I took the 41st Avenue bus to Joyce Station to catch the brand new Skytrain, built especially for Expo. It was so cool. The theme for Expo '86 was transportation, so as the host city, Vancouver decided to make a new form of public transit. The Skytrain was awesome.

"I love this," I thought as the doors slid open automatically to let me inside.

"*Bing, bing, bing.* The next stop is Nanaimo," chimed the voice over the speakers. This was so much cooler than the bus. Four stops later, I got off at Main and Terminal.

I saw Mike waiting for me in front of the Expo gate, looking just as excited as me about the day ahead. The sun was shining. We had nothing to do except hang out in pavilions and go on rides. Best day, ever!

Hundreds of people stood around at the gate, waiting to buy tickets. Crowds packed Expo all day, every day, and many visitors had travelled here from faraway countries. I felt so proud that Vancouver was my city, and that I wasn't a tourist, I was a local.

A couple of kids around my age stood with their families at the gate. Those poor guys. They had to hang out with their parents and brothers and sisters for the day. I felt sorry for them as I breezed past.

"Hey," said Mike as I walked up.

"Hey," I said back. We marched up to the gate and flashed our Expo passports, then paid for our all-day ride passes.

"First stop?" I asked Mike.

"Want to go to the Omnimax?"

"Sure," I agreed. Why not? We were standing right in front of it. The Omnimax showed IMAX movies inside a giant sphere that looked like a big golf ball. I had seen the movie lots of times, but I never got sick of it.

When the movie ended, Mike and I decided that we needed to hit some rides for the rest of the day.

"Hey, we should totally go on the Scream Machine and the Looping Starship before lunch. You know, just in case."

"In case what?" laughed Mike. "In case you puke?"

"Or you!"

"Good plan," said Mike.

The truth was that I wanted a chance to work up my nerve for the USSR Space Tower Parachute drop. I liked fast rides and I didn't even mind going upside down, but I was nervous about heights. The parachutes were seventy-two metres high in the sky and a straight freefall. Even though they made me nervous, there was no way I was chickening out. Luckily, the parachute drop was on the other side of the Expo grounds, so it would take us a while to get over there.

Mike and I rode the Looping Starship twice in a row, then once on the Scream Machine. It was a really hot day, so Mike suggested that we cool off on the Cariboo Log Chute. It was a water log ride with a big drop at the end guaranteed to get you soaking wet. I was boiling, so it sounded perfect.

We bee-lined past all the stuff that I normally did with my family. My mom always took forever in the country pavilions. My parents had to read every plaque and sign. The rest of us would stop to see the Roundhouse and Engine 374, the first CPR train to pull into Vancouver. We'd stare at the million-dollar gold coin, or sit in the concrete vehicles on Highway '86. I liked all that stuff, but not today. Today, I was my own man.

Mike and I sprinted around slow-moving families and tourists. We weren't messing around with pictures and gawking at statues or signposts; we were serious about rides. Having a season pass meant that we could come back any day we wanted to do all that stuff.

Even waiting in line for the log chute was fun because you could watch all the people getting wet on the big hill. There was only one problem. When we raced over this way, we missed the whole middle of the Expo area. The log chute stood directly in the shadow of the parachute ride. The screams of people riding on the parachutes were a big distraction, at least for me. Those people sounded terrified. This was not the kind of scream that you let out during the scary part of a movie, or on the hill of a roller coaster. This one was more like an afraid-for-your-life sort of shriek.

After cooling off on the log chute, Mike suggested we go for lunch. I didn't know if he was also delaying on the parachutes, but I was all for it. The only problem was that I felt a little sick anticipating the parachute. Food wasn't at the top of my list, but I was ready to postpone the ride, so off we went to the McBarge, the coolest place to eat at Expo. It was a McDonald's that was on a real floating boat. How awesome was that?

"Hey," said Mike, "better be careful what you order, because you might be seeing it again on the parachute ride."

"Ha, ha," I said sarcastically. "I thought I heard you screaming on the Scream Machine, or was that the little girls sitting behind us?"

Reaching the front of the line, Mike stepped up to order. He got a Big Mac meal and a soft served ice cream cone. Then it was my turn.

"I'll have a Quarter Pounder meal, please," I said. "And an ice cream." I paid with my own money, which felt great. We got our food and sat down. Mike started eating his ice cream right away. When I looked at him funny he said, "Well, it's not like my mom is here to say that I have to finish my lunch before I get dessert."

No kidding! I gobbled down my ice cream too. Total freedom!

"So, parachutes?" I asked. Maybe Mike would come up with an alternative. The lineup started about twenty feet away, so it wouldn't be easy to come up with a different plan.

"Yeah," said Mike. He didn't sound all that keen either.

We stood in line for the ride. Neither one of us said anything for a while. We listened to the screams and moved forward slowly towards our fate. My hamburger was beginning to churn strangely in my stomach. Eating the ice cream first might have been a bad idea too. Or maybe it was the big cup of pop that was making me queasy?

"I bet the view from up there is amazing," I said. We both looked up.

"If all you want is the view, you could skip the parachutes and just go up to the observation area at the top," joked Mike. Was he serious? He didn't look all that well.

Well, I wasn't going to be the one to come out and say that I wanted to leave. Nice try, Mike, I thought. "Nope, that's lame. I want to feel the rush."

"Me too," he said. "We can do this all day if we want."

We didn't say anything else until we reached the very front of the line. The parachutes held two people each. We walked over together as a tough-looking guy strapped us into our parachute.

"This is awesome," said Mike in a flat voice. I couldn't even get out a word. It felt like my Quarter Pounder was halfway up my throat. The parachute left the ground, pulling us slowly into the air.

It turned out the view was amazing, just like I'd said. I could see all over Expo and across False Creek. For a split second, I forgot how terrified I felt. I had such an incredible perspective on the city that it took my breath away in a good way.

Then my breath was taken away in a bad way. A very bad way.

The plunge came much faster than I expected. My body dropped to the earth and my stomach stayed in the clouds. Then my stomach caught up and that was not a good feeling. Would I lose my lunch? Luckily, I managed to keep it down.

Before I knew it, the ride was over. As I worked to swallow the big lump of hamburger in my throat, I was happy that the buckle system was complicated because it gave me a moment to recover before I had to stand up. As I wobbled away, my knees buckled, my shins shivered like jelly, and my ankles tumbled sideways. I turned and looked at Mike.

"Man, that was so . . ." he mumbled.

"Totally, yeah . . ." I stammered.

"Hey, do you want to go check out the million-dollar gold coin?"

"For sure," I said. "I wouldn't mind seeing the Roundhouse again."

We turned around, and walked slowly through the crowd.

What do we know for sure?

Vancouver put on a big one-hundredth birthday party in 1986, and invited the world to come for the celebration. It had been one hundred years since Vancouver officially became a city in 1886 and Expo '86 was a great opportunity for the city to show how far it had come in one century.

Prince Charles, Princess Diana, and Prime Minister Brian Mulroney opened the fair on May 2, 1986. The city had transformed an old CPR rail yard and a bunch of ugly industrial land into one hundred and seventy-three acres of fun. Many people felt it was a coming-of-age party for Vancouver, introducing the city to the world as a sophisticated urban centre.

More than twenty-two million people walked through the gates of Expo. Even though the fair lost approximately three hundred and eleven million dollars, tourism increased, Vancouver received a lot of positive media coverage around the world, and the city gained some interesting new buildings and the Skytrain.

In the story, Eric mentioned the Skytrain, which was built for Expo. The Skytrain has been expanded four times since 1986, including the recent Canada Line extension. He also talked about a giant sphere that was an Omnimax theatre. Can you guess what that turned into? It reopened as Science World in 1990.

BC Place was constructed for Expo, as was Canada Place. The Roundhouse mentioned in the story was restored for Expo and today is a busy downtown community centre. Expo '86 transformed the landscape of Vancouver.

If you have eagle eyes, you might even be able to spot the McBarge that served Eric and Mike their lunch that day. If you are driving along Dollarton Highway in North Vancouver, you'll see it abandoned but still afloat on the opposite side of Indian Arm.

Today high-rises and condos cover the Expo lands, but for five months in 1986, it was a world party.

As for Eric Butler, he told me that he is much braver on rides today than he was in 1986. I know that's true, because he is my husband and I have shared dozens of roller coasters with him and he never screams or chickens out. In fact, he grew up to be a firefighter and deals with heights and scary situations all the time. Eric left Vancouver for almost ten years when he was playing professional basketball in Europe, but always knew he'd come home to Vancouver. He still points out the McBarge to our kids when we see it up Indian Arm.

Eric remembers Expo '86 as one of most exciting parts of his childhood. That summer, he and his friends went to the grounds almost every day. He said that it felt like both he and Vancouver grew up together that year.

Nora (holding Flat Miga) standing between Miga
and Quatchi, the 2010 Olympic mascots.

The Day I Danced for the Entire World

Nora O'Callaghan, age ten
Vancouver/North Vancouver, 2010

So this is what the Olympic spirit feels like, I thought.

My little brother, Roger, my mom, and I had just arrived at the Vancouver Olympic Centre for our audition to participate in the opening ceremonies of the 2010 Paralympic Games. When my mom had suggested we try out, I wasn't too sure I wanted to do it. I didn't know what to expect. I worried that everyone would be watching me and that I might mess up. My mom reassured me that there would be so many people trying out that no one would be watching just me.

I didn't believe her completely until we arrived. I saw cars everywhere and crowds of kids and grown-ups. Mom was right. I could probably dance in a chicken costume and nobody would notice me.

"We were lucky to get parking," my mom said. She was right. It was super crowded.

"Fiona will be sorry she missed this," I told my mom. My little sister, Fiona, had decided not to come. She was nervous about performing too. "You can tell her all about it, Nora," Mom said. "Maybe she'll change her mind."

We walked inside and registered. I saw people everywhere, gathered around talking or rushing somewhere or practising different dance routines. I could hear three or four different songs playing at the same time. It was chaos.

Right away, we split into groups to learn a dance. When they told us we had to learn a whole routine, I became a bit worried again. What if I couldn't do it?

"All you can do is try your best," my mom told me. "You are a good dancer. You'll be great."

As soon as I watched the routine a couple of times, I felt a lot better. It wasn't so hard. Once I had practised a bit, I could do it without one mistake. Even my little brother Roger could do it. Actually, he was pretty good. He was only six years old, the youngest you could be to audition. If he could remember the routine, so could I.

The organizers announced that we would be split into smaller groups of five for a performance. Yikes. I didn't know anyone in my group, but I was happy to see that they were all girls my age.

"Are you nervous?" I asked the girl next to me. We were sitting in the bleachers waiting for our turn, watching a group of five women practising their routine.

"Yeah, sort of," she said. "They look so small out there."

She was right. When we were learning all together, it wasn't so scary, but with only five people on the floor it looked a little more nerve-wracking.

"I think it'll be okay," I said. I hoped that I sounded more certain than I felt.

"We'll do great," she said. "My name's Emma, by the way."

"I'm Nora," I said. We talked a little bit while we waited for our group to be called.

Emma was eleven and super friendly. By the time it was our turn, we were laughing and having fun. "Good luck," I told Emma as we walked out together into the middle of the big, empty dance floor.

My stomach started to tickle a little bit standing there, waiting for the music. We faced a table of people who were taking notes on each of us. They stared at us, smiling. I hoped I wouldn't mix up the steps. I looked at Emma and she smiled.

Suddenly, the music started. We were dancing. The butterflies in my tummy disappeared as soon as I was moving. I was doing it! I finished the whole routine, no problem. As soon as it ended, I felt great. I found Roger and my mom.

"I hope I get chosen," I told my mom. "That would be so cool."

■ ■ ■

After the auditions in October, it felt like we had to wait forever to hear if we'd have a chance to perform at the opening ceremonies. Finally, in December, we found out. They picked me! I jumped all around my living room with excitement. I was actually going to be a part of the Games! Roger and my mom would perform too. Even Fiona was going to join us. When she heard us talking about how much fun we'd had at the auditions, she'd changed her mind and tried out a few days later.

We had rehearsals scheduled for every Sunday in January at the Agriplex in Cloverdale. When I saw Emma at the first rehearsal, I was so happy. If I had a friend there, it would be so much more fun. I had a good time at every single rehearsal. We found out that we'd line up to form an aisle for the Paralympic athletes to enter the stadium. We would get to see the athletes up close. I couldn't wait.

The closer the Games came, the more the whole city caught the spirit. It was thrilling to know that I was going to join the fun. The Olympic torch relay was especially exciting in my family because my mom ran with the torch in the Northwest Territories. I didn't see it, but we did watch our family friend Blair Horn run through North Vancouver. That was really funny because my brother had a chance to test Olympic security. He was so excited to see Blair that he tried to dash out to say hi and touch the torch. Apparently, that wasn't allowed.

My family participated in all kinds of Olympic events and activities. My mom suggested that I keep a journal to write down all the fun activities we were doing. I also made my own Flat Miga, named after the character in the *Flat Stanley* book. It was a laminated cut-out of the Miga mascot that I could take everywhere we went. We took pictures of it everywhere we went, and asked people to autograph it. My Flat Miga was my constant companion, always in my backpack within easy reach.

Once the Olympics started, the energy in Vancouver was out of this world. My favourite part of the opening ceremonies was watching Nelly Furtado and Bryan Adams sing. Seeing the opening ceremonies was super thrilling because I kept thinking about how I would be in the next opening ceremonies in Vancouver.

We went to as many Olympic events as we could, in Vancouver, in Richmond, and up at Whistler. My brother and sister and I talked a lot about what sports we would do in the Olympics if we could. I would love to be a figure skater, but the women's freestyle skiing was the most fun to watch.

My family had tickets to the closing ceremonies. After watching the men's hockey game on TV and seeing Canada win gold, we hurried downtown and joined the huge crowd at BC Place to celebrate. Out of all the amazing and fantastic things we'd seen over the two weeks of the Olympics, the closing ceremonies were the very best. The whole city was celebrating. If we could have bottled the energy in BC Place, I bet Vancouver could have had free electricity for a year.

I couldn't believe that in twelve days I would be in BC Place, on that very same floor, as an entertainer for the Paralympics opening ceremonies.

■ ■ ■

Once the Olympics wrapped up, our rehearsals started again. We had some long, long days. We had practice on Sunday, Wednesday, Thursday, and Friday. Luckily, it was spring break so I didn't miss any school. Or maybe that wasn't so lucky! Some days, we rehearsed for almost eight hours straight, which was exhausting. Even though it was tiring sometimes, it was so much fun. All the kids ate together and the food was so tasty. Plus, we had lots of time in between practices to talk. Emma and I had a great time, plus I made friends with other great girls like Georgia, Zoë, Selena, and Francesca. We were working hard, but we could also hang out lots. We received our costumes for the show on the last day of rehearsals. They were so Olympic—fleecy, red and white with maple leaves. I loved mine and I felt so proud when I put it on. I just hoped that I was ready for the big show.

■ ■ ■

I woke up on the morning of March 12 with my heart beating a million miles an hour. It wasn't just the date of the Paralympics opening ceremonies, it was also my tenth birthday. It felt like the most perfect day ever.

Nora trying sledge hockey.
O'CALLAGHAN FAMILY COLLECTION

For the first time in my life, the most important celebration on March 12 was *not* my birthday. I barely thought about it as we hurried to prepare for the opening ceremonies. Even though I was wishing the minutes would pass by faster, I was also getting nervous. If feeling a little bit anxious is like one butterfly fluttering, then I had a butterfly party in my stomach. They were going crazy in there.

Finally, the time came to go down to BC Place and get ready for the show. Fiona, Roger, and I pulled on our costumes and met our groups in the big tents set up for us outside of the stadium. I saw people in blue Olympic jackets everywhere I looked. They were so helpful, answering questions and making sure we knew what we were doing.

BC Place was filling up. It was almost sold out. Thousands of people waited in the stands, ready to watch us. When I thought about the number of people out there, I nearly couldn't breathe. I wasn't even thinking about the television cameras and all the people who would be watching in their homes.

Someone came around with little earbuds to put in our ears. They were connected to receivers that we wore on our backs. With the earbuds, we could hear our coach tell us what to do next.

"Am I putting mine in right?" I asked a blue jacket person. "They don't feel very comfortable."

She checked mine, but they were in right. I guess they weren't meant to fit into kids' ears because they sort of hurt.

"Do yours feel funny too?" I asked Fiona.

She was fiddling with hers, just like I was. "Yeah," she said. "But I want them anyway."

"For sure," I said, "I don't want to make a mistake." I had to stop trying to make them more comfortable because the Blue Jackets were handing out the pom-poms we had to wave while the athletes were coming out. They were neat because they had little lights inside them. When they were turned on, they blinked and flashed. And the best part was that we could take them home with us.

"Alright kids, you'll be heading onto the floor in two minutes; two minutes to showtime," said one of the producers as she walked around and checked on us. "Make sure your pom-poms are working. Let's see lots of energy and smiles. Listen for directions in your earbuds. Most of all, have fun!"

We stepped into our formation and waited for the signal to start moving into BC Place.

"I'm so nervous," I whispered to Emma, who was standing behind me. "It's so loud in there. What if we can't hear what they tell us? What if I take a wrong turn just as the camera zooms in on me?"

"They have so much to look at that I don't think they'll notice if we make a mistake," she said.

"I just don't want to fall, or go in the wrong direction or something," I told her.

Emma didn't get a chance to answer because we were on the move. We were led through the tents into BC Place. The feeling inside was electric. All the hairs on my arms stood up and the butterflies in my stomach kicked up a storm. My legs felt wobbly and a bit weak. There was so much happening in the staging area that we had to squeeze past other groups who were also getting ready to go on. Voices shouting directions came from everywhere.

"Prepare to walk out. Remember to form the aisle for the athletes in straight lines," said the voice in my earbud. "Heading out in three, two . . . one!"

I wasn't sure my legs would carry me, but they did. I just focused on the fleecy jacket moving in front of me.

The crowd inside the stadium was so loud that I wondered if the roof could pop from too much sound. The music soared, people cheered, and I saw flashes from cameras everywhere. I took a deep breath, found my spot, and waved my pom-poms.

As soon as we were in place, the Paralympians started coming up through the aisle we formed. We danced on either side as they filed into BC Place. We waved our pom-poms, danced, and gave high-fives all at the same time. I was so proud of our athletes.

I couldn't wait to watch the events and see how the Canadians would do in competition.

Once my nerves settled down, I took a moment to look around me. It seemed like every seat was filled. Vancouver was alive with excitement and pride. I could feel all the positive emotions in the building swirling around me. The butterflies had taken off and they'd left behind a happy glow.

A television camera operator came up beside me.

"Woohoo!" I shouted. "Go Canada!"

I danced for almost an hour on the floor of BC Place, but it felt like it was over in seconds. I had no birthday cake to eat, and no candles to blow out on my tenth birthday, but Vancouver was throwing me the biggest and best party ever. It was the most exciting day of my whole life.

What do we know for sure?

What a fantastic way to celebrate a birthday! Right after she came offstage, Nora O'Callaghan and her brother and sister were handed gorgeous participation medals in honour of their hard work as volunteers in the Paralympics.

The Paralympics is a multi-sport event for athletes with physical disabilities, which takes place immediately following the Olympic Games. For Nora and her family, it was one of the most thrilling events of the Games. The Vancouver 2010 Olympic and Paralympic Games brought a gigantic party to our city. Thousands of Vancouver area kids participated in the Games. In fact, five thousand local people performed in the Paralympic opening ceremonies along with Nora and her family. What was your favourite part of the celebrations?

When Vancouver was awarded the 2010 Olympic and Paralympic Games, there was some controversy about whether it was the right decision for the city. Putting on an international event of that size is expensive and some Vancouverites suggested that the money spent on the Games and their security could be put to better use. Despite these misgivings, most of the city caught Olympic fever once the torch was lit.

The Games took years of planning and hard work, but hosting the Olympics and Paralympics left our city with a legacy of more than just memories. The sports facilities constructed for the Games will allow future Olympians to train in the most advanced facilities. If you want to see where the Olympians competed, go out to the Richmond Olympic Oval or visit the Vancouver Olympic Centre in Riley Park. They were both constructed especially for the Games.

The Own the Podium program, launched for these Games, provided more money and support for Canadian athletes than ever before. Thanks in large part to that program, Canada won fourteen gold medals, the most ever won by a host nation. Other benefits of hosting the Olympics are tougher to measure, such as how many kids were inspired to join a new sport or try harder at an old one. I wonder how many kids made the Olympics or Paralympics a new goal during the Games. Maybe you were one of them?

Nora was. She told me that her new idol is Ashleigh McIvor, the Canadian freestyle skier who was the first ever gold-medal winner in women's ski-cross in Vancouver. Nora skis at Whistler with her family every winter, so maybe we'll see her competing in the Winter Games one day.

Nora had another special connection to the Vancouver 2010 Games. Her grandmother, Mary McNeil, is Member of the BC Legislative Assembly for Vancouver-False Creek and was appointed Minister of State for the Olympics. Nora told me it was pretty cool to have her grandmother so involved in the success of the Games.

Nora is the daughter of a friend of mine. It was fun to meet her and hear all about her Olympic and Paralympic memories. One of the reasons that Nora was able to remember so many details of what she did during the Olympics was that she kept a detailed journal. She captured her memories as she was creating them. Do you keep a journal? Think of the second story in this book about Captain George Vancouver. We know a lot about his discovery of Vancouver because he kept a journal. Right now, you are creating history yourself. Why not write it all down? You can scribble in a notebook, or start a blog and upload pictures. Maybe someday I'll be reading *your* journals.

Molly on her bike, 2010.

Biking Backwards

Molly Butler, age eight
Vancouver, 2010

As soon as the three o'clock bell rang, my best friend Maya ran over and hooked her arm through mine. "Molly, let's go out to the playground," she said.

"I can't today," I told her. "My mom and I are going for a bike ride."

"Cool, where are you guys going?" she asked.

"On a kid's history tour of Vancouver," I told her. "I've been reading all the stories my mom's been writing and she's going to show me where they happened."

"Alright, see you tomorrow then," she said. "Have fun!"

"Bye," I waved. I grabbed my backpack and helmet and went out to see if my mom was waiting. She'd already unlocked my bike and it looked like she was ready to go.

My mom had been working writing the book you are reading now. You should have seen our house. It looked like the local history section of the library exploded in our family room. There were books and old pictures all over the place. She spent months driving all of us crazy with her "interesting facts" about Vancouver. Some of them were interesting. Some of them were not.

I really liked hearing the stories about kids. One day I was asking my mom questions about where August Jack's house was in Stanley Park.

"Is it still there?" I asked her.

"Nope," she said. "His house is long gone."

"What about Minnie McCord's house? Is hers still there?"

"Nope again. There's a hotel there now. Hey, do you want to go on a tour with me? I can show you where lots of the stories took place. What do you say?"

"Sure," I said. And today was the day.

■ ■ ■

My mom and I biked around the seawall.

"I still remember seeing Vancouver for the first time," mom told me. "I was fourteen years old and I had just moved here. I thought it was the most beautiful place I had ever been. My uncle drove me up Cypress Mountain and told me to look down at my new hometown. It sparkled."

"It is really beautiful," I said.

"It's a bit different for you, though," Mom said. "I got to see Vancouver with fresh eyes. You grew up here, so it's harder for you to see the city in a new way. Stop here for a second."

We pulled off to the side of the seawall and got off our bikes. We were standing next to the Olympic Village.

"Do you remember what it looked like here, before these buildings were finished?" my mom asked me.

"Yeah," I answered. "Well, sort of. I remember when there was just tons of dirt."

"Okay, now close your eyes. I want you to picture it in your head the way that it looked when it was just dirt. Can you do it?"

"Yep," I said. "Hey, can we go for gelato after this?"

"Maybe. Alright, now I want you to use your imagination to see this area with really fresh eyes. I want you to think about how it might have looked fifty years ago, or one hundred years ago. Tell me what you see."

"Okay," I said. "I imagine old buildings and people in old-fashioned clothes. I hear horse hooves clopping along on dirt roads."

"Pretty good, Moll," my mom said. "Actually, it was all industrial buildings here and tidal mud flats. There was a slaughterhouse, so the air was really smelly. There were huge dangerous log booms floating in the water that kids used to play on. Sometimes change is a good thing. Now there's the seawall and parks here for us to enjoy instead."

"A slaughterhouse? For killing animals? Ugh," I said. "Let's keep going."

"Sure," said mom. "Let's see if we can steer your sensitive stomach past the gelato."

We stayed on the seawall, pedalling past Science World. As we biked, my mom talked some more.

"Do you remember being down in this area during the Olympics?" mom asked me.

"Of course. This was where the Yaletown stage was, right?"

"You got it. When your dad was a kid here, these were the Expo '86 lands. This area was covered with pavilions and rides. Vancouver has hosted the whole world twice right where we are biking."

We kept on going, but as I pedalled I was thinking how strange it would have been for some of the Vancouver kids I read about in mom's stories to see events like the Olympics, or to ride on a roller coaster at Expo. William Roedde was super excited just to ride in a car. That sure isn't a treat for me. Long trips in our car made me feel sick.

When we got to English Bay, we stopped for a drink of water.

"There are so many stories about Vancouver kids that I couldn't write about in the book. See that hotel behind us covered with ivy?" mom asked.

"*The Sylvia Hotel*," I read. "It's beautiful."

"The man who opened it in 1912 named it after his daughter. Neat, huh?"

"I would love to have my own hotel. Welcome to the Molly Inn, enjoy your stay."

"I bet your hotel would be a lot of fun, Moll, but based on the state of your room, I don't think I'd count on great maid service," said Mom.

"You're probably right," I said. "I'd rather spend my days right here on the beach."

"You wouldn't be alone. This beach has always been one of the most popular spots in the city, even when there were no roads to get here. People used to walk in on a trail through the forest. Vancouver's first lifeguard worked here. His name was Joe Fortes and came here from the West Indies. He taught hundreds of Vancouver kids how to swim in this water, and he saved quite a few from drowning too."

"Isn't there a restaurant named Joe Fortes?" I asked.

"Yep," Mom said, "and a library too. They're both named after him. Let's keep moving."

We rode into Stanley Park. I told my mom that my legs were getting tired. She told me that Bertha Patterson walked three miles carrying three squirming hens in a burlap bag. "I guess I can't complain that my schoolbag is heavy, then?" I asked her.

"Nope," she laughed.

We biked past Siwash Rock and the plaque for Pauline Johnson.

"Remind me to read you the legend of the Rock," Mom shouted over her shoulder as we kept going. "It's in Pauline Johnson's book. You'd like it."

We kept going until we were nearly at the Lions Gate Bridge.

"So remember how I made you close your eyes to picture what False Creek might have looked like a hundred years ago?" Mom said. I nodded. "The neat thing about Stanley Park is that you don't have to imagine. Look around. This is what all the land around Vancouver was like before the city sprang up. Let's leave our bikes for a second and step into the forest."

We walked about a dozen steps into the woods.

"Take a deep breath," Mom instructed.

I did. It was earthy and wet. It smelled like dirt and moss.

"I bet we are in August Jack's backyard right now," she said. "Let's take a little walk and think about August Jack and what his life was like here."

As I stepped over the fallen logs and slipped on the rotting leaves, I thought about him. I imagined what it would be like living in the middle of this big forest, with no grocery stores for getting food, no lights, no doctors, no cars, no bridge overhead. I thought about books I had read about time travel and I wondered if I could stumble into a time warp that would transport me back to Chaythoos. I got ready to run away from Chulwalsh, August Jack's bull. I imagined him crashing through the undergrowth towards me. I listened for a moment. No bull. I guess it was still 2011.

I walked back to where my mom was standing.

"Alright Molly, imagine this. I want you to go over to that tree right there and climb up it a little bit." She waited until I was a few feet off the ground. "Okay, now look out towards the water. Pretend that it is 1792 and you live in Chaythoos. You have never seen anything on the water bigger than a dug-out canoe, but right now you can see a ship cruising up the First Narrows all by itself with no paddles. It's George Vancouver's yawl. You are watching the very first Europeans to come here and they are bringing with them some of the changes that will create the Vancouver of 2011. How do you feel?"

I peered out through the trees and pictured the ship. "Nervous and scared, I guess," I said, "but maybe a bit excited and curious too."

"I bet that's exactly how they felt, Moll," my mom said. "Let's go back to our bikes."

We rode around Brockton Point to where the Nine O'Clock Gun stands and parked our bikes against a bench. We went and sat on the edge of the seawall and dangled our feet over the side. My mom pulled out some green grapes and we took turns grabbing them off their stems and popping them in our mouths.

"So Molly, you can pretty much see it all from here," my mom said.

"Like what?" I asked.

"Vancouver's history is all laid out for you, but it's buried underneath the modern city. You need to think of the stories and then put on fresh eyes to see it. Over there is the Bayshore Hotel and that's where Kanaka Ranch used to be, where Minnie McCord lived with her family. The *Komagata Maru* was anchored in the harbour here for two months in 1914. And in the distance over there you can see Gastown, which is where the city of Vancouver was born."

"And where Madeline lived with Gassy Jack," I said. "If I got married at twelve years old, like her, I'd only have four more years to be a kid."

"No husbands for you for a while," said my mom, looking horrified. "Some traditions are best left in history."

"No kidding," I laughed.

"Can you imagine what downtown looked like on fire one hundred and twenty-five years ago? Picture flames filling the sky, stretching across the whole waterfront. That's what the First Nations living on the North Shore would have seen. They paddled across this water to rescue hundreds of people, including lots of kids."

"Vancouver has changed so much," I said, looking towards the skyscrapers of downtown.

"I wonder how it will change in your lifetime," my mom said. "I have a present for you." She reached into her bag and pulled out a nicely bound leather notebook.

"What's that?" I asked.

"It's a place for you to put your own stories," she said.

I laughed. "I don't have any stories like that," I said. "I didn't escape a big fire, or have my house chopped down to make room for a road."

"Do you know where we sitting right now?" mom asked me.

"On the seawall?"

"Yes, but we are also sitting right where Xwá.y̓xway or Whoi Whoi village used to be. Elizabeth Silvey came to the potlatch here, remember? If you had asked her at the time if that was special or interesting, she would have told you that it was plain old everyday life."

"Really?" I asked.

"Sure. One thing I learned when I was writing this book is that we all have stories to tell. You are making history right now. You are a Vancouver kid."

I took the notebook out of her hand and opened the front cover. Inside were blank, lined pages.

"What's your story?" she asked me.

Acknowledgements

This book would not have been possible without the help and support of many wonderful people. I am most grateful for the Vancouver kids of the past and present who inspired and guided me in my quest to tell their stories. I was able to speak personally to some of the kids who made their way into this book, but many of the children's voices had to travel a great distance through time to land in these pages. I am grateful to the kids who spoke the words that were recorded and I am indebted to those who valued them enough to record them.

As I sifted through material at the public library, archives, and on the Internet, the children of the city jumped out at me. Vancouver's history has been a constant topic of conversation for me, in coffee shops, at dinner parties, and with friends. Generous people have offered me the stories of their grandparents, aunts and uncles, or their own childhood tales of adventure and courage. I wish I could include all the stories I've come across, but every single anecdote or story I've heard has played a part in the journey of this book.

I want to thank Ruth Linka and Brindle & Glass for offering me this wonderful opportunity. I also owe a huge debt to Linda Goyette, my relentlessly positive and encouraging editor. Linda had the uncanny ability to sense when I needed a supportive e-mail, or when I simply needed space to gets words on the page. Her thoughtful, kind, and intelligent edits were a gift. Tara Saracuse was a fantastic resource, patient e-mail correspondent and lovely lunch companion. Thanks to everyone at Brindle & Glass.

I used numerous sources for research purposes. Without the hard work and dedication of historians and other authors, I couldn't have put this book together. I am in their debt. I am grateful for the many helpful librarians in the public library system; Leslie Mobbs and the professional staff at the City of Vancouver Archives; Vanessa Campbell at the Squamish Nation; Jean Barman, Arthur Ray, Robert Muckle, Janet Bingham, Hugh Johnson, Eve Lazarus, Lee Maracle, Lisa Smedman, the Museum of Vancouver; the Museum of Anthropology at the University of British Columbia; Robert McDonald, W. Kaye Lamb, the brilliant volunteers and docents at Roedde House; Keith Beedie, Mas Yamamoto, Joy and Randy May, Sarah Kato, Dawnne Blaker, Judy and Sandy Bau, Bira Bindra, Molly, Michael and Nora O'Callaghan, Paul Yee, Molly Butler, Eric Butler, and Jane Butler.

I am most thankful for the love and never-ending support of my family and friends. My parents, Judy and Bryan McKnight, and my brother PJ, have been unwavering in their encouragement. My husband, Eric, is the only reason I could say yes to writing this book. I knew I could count on his help, his brilliant brain, and his unwavering love. He is the best thing that ever happened to me. I also have to thank our three kids, Molly, Finley, and Lucas, for being inspiring, patient, and all-around amazing. They are my favourite Vancouver kids.

Lesley McKnight moved to Vancouver as a child and lives there with her husband and three children. For the past ten years she has been a freelance researcher and writer, and her articles have been published in places like *The Globe & Mail* and the *Vancouver Courier*.